WALL
PARA
R AF F

3 5392

AP

PARADISE CREEK

A previous autobiographical novel by Leo
Walmsley was set beside a Cornish creek. Daphne
du Maurier wrote of it, " Leo Walmsley gives the
reader a true story, classic in its simplicity, of a
man and a girl who possess nothing in life but love
for each other and faith in the future ".

The opening chapters of this new novel are
called " Paradise Lost ". The home beside the
creek, an old army hut, is derelict; love has
temporarily left the author's life and with it his
wife. But he schemes to end this unhappy state
of affairs and to re-create the home beside the cove
to which his four children can come, at least for
the holidays. The first essential is a dinghy, the
second is help with his ambitious plans to re-design
the hut. Next he cannot resist a cabin cruiser with
a converted Austin Seven engine which is to play
its part in the adventures of the children's first
exciting visit. But essentially this is a love story,
a quest for and a discovery of happiness. The
dramatic events which give to the final chapters
the title " Paradise Regained " are left to
the readers to discover for themselves.

By The Same Author

Novels

THREE FEVERS
PHANTOM LOBSTER
FOREIGNERS
SALLY LUNN
LOVE IN THE SUN
MASTER MARINER
THE GOLDEN WATERWHEEL
THE HAPPY ENDING
SOUND OF THE SEA

Autobiography

SO MANY LOVES

Travel

INVISIBLE CARGO

Essays

BRITISH PORTS AND HARBOURS
YORKSHIRE AND LANCASHIRE
(FESTIVAL OF BRITAIN GUIDE)

Play

SALLY LUNN

LEO WALMSLEY

Paradise Creek

A
TRUE STORY 35392

ARBROATH
PUBLIC
LIBRARY

COLLINS
ST JAMES'S PLACE
LONDON

19. AUG. 1969

FIRST IMPRESSION   MAY, 1963
SECOND   ,,   JUNE, 1963
THIRD   ,,   AUGUST, 1963

ACKNOWLEDGMENTS

I am grateful to the Public Trustee and the Society of Authors for permission to use the quotation from *Man and Superman* by Bernard Shaw and also to Methuen and Co. Ltd. and the Viking Press for permission to reproduce *Resume* by Dorothy Parker.

© LEO WALMSLEY, 1963
PRINTED IN GREAT BRITAIN
COLLINS CLEAR-TYPE PRESS: LONDON AND GLASGOW

*Affectionately to Fred Smith
whose kindness and encouragement
in the long years of our association
never failed*

CONTENTS

BOOK ONE

Paradise Lost

I

A BOOK of mine, with the rapturous title *Love in the Sun*, was published in this country in August of the fateful year 1939, three weeks before the start of Hitler's war.

It was the story, based closely on fact, of how my wife and I, then very poor, found an empty and derelict army hut on a lonely creek near Fowey, in Cornwall, rented it for three shillings a week, and made it into a home; making our own furniture, chiefly from driftwood and ships' dunnage, growing or catching most of our food, and supporting ourselves otherwise by collecting and selling marine and other animals to a zoological laboratory.

Love in the Sun got a Press that might have turned the head of any struggling author. A fortnight after publication it was at the top of *The Observer*'s best-seller list. It looked as though we were going to make a fortune.

It was six years since we had left our humble Cornish home. The sale of the film rights of my novel, *Three Fevers*, to Arthur Rank (this was his Lordship's first film and the price was £300) had enabled us to buy forty-two acres of rough land on the edge of the now famous Fylingdale's Moor, two and a half miles inland from the sea and my native village of Robin Hood's Bay, to which, in *Three Fevers*, I had given the fictitious name, Bramblewick. With a mortgage we had converted an existing barn into a house which had every modern convenience except electricity.

Our family, started with the birth of a daughter in Cornwall, had grown to four with another daughter and two sons. It was, I often thought (perhaps too complacently) the ideal life we were living.

13

On the fly-leaf of *Love in the Sun* I had quoted the second verse of that lovely song from *As You Like It*:

> Who doth ambition shun
> And loves to live i' th' sun
> Seeking the food he eats,
> And pleased with what he gets,
> Come hither, come hither, come hither:
> Here shall he see
> No enemy
> But winter and rough weather.

That, in spirit, was as applicable to our Yorkshire home as it was to Cornwall, although we had a professionally built, stone-walled, slate-roofed house with so many of the amenities of civilisation.

Except for one or two farmhouses, there were no other buildings in sight.

The place was a paradise for children. A clear babbling stream ran from the moor through our land, continuing over a twelve-foot cliff and waterfall into an oak wood. The wood was not our property, but we had a right of way. Here, in spring, daffodils grew in profusion at the stream's edge. There were oaks, alders, ash and mountain ash, and on our own land too. In one place we had dammed the stream and made a long pool, deep enough to float a small flat-bottomed boat I had built. There was a patch of clean white sand nearby, and I made a swing from a branch of a thick gnarled oak which we christened The Greenwood Tree.

There were trout in the stream, too small for serious angling. The children made pets of them, and gave them names. There were water voles and a pair of water ouzels who sometimes could be seen walking along the pool's bed, hunting caddis and mayfly larvæ, and with their mossy domed nest under the waterfall.

It *was* the perfect life! We were not, however, blind to the fact that our children would grow up. One best-seller would not be enough to see them to maturity. Fortunately, within a mile of our home was an excellent co-ed school, run by friends of ours, the Bradleys, with views on education more or less similar to our own. This would cater for their primary education at least, after which it would be Bedales or Dartington or some such modern progressive boarding-school, which would not of course be cheap.

Everything in the garden was lovely those first two weeks of August 1939; and a year before I had been personally assured by no less a prophet than H. G. Wells at a memorable lunch he had given me at his house in Hanover Terrace, that Hitler was only a gigantic bluffer, that there was no real likelihood of war.

But the war came. The sirens sounded for the first time. The blitz did not happen. This was only the start of the phoney war. But the booksellers were scared, chary of investing more capital in books when at any time their shops and stocks might be blown sky high. The sales of *Love in the Sun* stopped dead.

We weren't going to make that fortune after all!

II

WE HAD our anxieties in those early days of the war. Who hadn't? But for the first time in our married life we were not worried about money. We were not going to be rich, but so long as we were not extravagant we were assured of a decent income for the next two or three years. The house and the land were now virtually our own, and we had no debts. Besides I had a sneaking optimism that Hitler would soon realise that he had bitten off more than he could chew, and would angle for an early peace.

One serious blow was that under pressure of parents, our friends had decided to evacuate their school to Cumberland. It was good-bye to our hopes of our children getting the education we had planned for them.

Personally, I did not regard this matter of education as of such great importance. If the blitz were to come, or we were to be invaded, the first thing was to see to the physical safety of the children. We must have an air raid shelter, an extra large supply of food. As the house originally planned and built had proved a little cramped for our expanding family we had extended it with a two-story annexe. This was built of timber with a flat asphalt roof, perfect tinder for an incendiary bomb, and within yards of it was a thicket of furze, bramble and bracken. The clearing of this thicket was one of our first war-time jobs, a precaution that undoubtedly saved the house from destruction when, later, the incendiaries came.

Thus there was plenty to do, inside and outside, to furnish some relief to anxiety. We decided to have two of our relatively level fields ploughed up so that they could be sown with oats in the spring. They had to be cleared and fenced. There was the garden; the potatoes to be lifted, dried and clamped, blackberries to be picked and made into jam; turf to be cut, stacked and led down to the house with the pony and trap; firewood to be collected and sawn into logs for the big room fire.

So in spite of the war, we were still reasonably happy. We were not ostriches. None of us knew what lay ahead. We had been warned not to underrate the power and intentions of the enemy. We had been told officially that the war could be expected to last at least three years. That the attempts to blockade our sea-borne supply lines would be intensified. That food and other commodities would grow scarcer, that rationing was inevitable, that we must all be prepared for sacrifices, discomforts, hardships, perils . . .

Yet if anyone had told us then that in the course of the war our own marriage would break up—that my wife and I would part—we would have held each other's hands, like a happy bride and bridegroom being photographed outside the church, and smiled.

No, we did not know what lay ahead!

III

I HAVE written two books, both published in the post-war years as novels, in the first of which I told the story of the making of our Yorkshire home and our life there up to the second year of the war, when a combination of circumstances obliged us to give it up and move to Pembrokeshire. The beaches had been closed. The Moor was to become an artillery range and battle training ground. The fields which we had started to cultivate were to be open-cast mined to win a bed of gannister, a precious material in demand for munition works.

In the second book I told the story of our life in Wales; how we made a derelict mansion habitable, solving the problem of our children's education by starting a school of our own, and reclaiming the long neglected land which went with the mansion which I had called Castle Druid.

Both books were written in the same style as *Love in the Sun*. They were based to a very great extent on fact. But I gave fictitious names to places and people. I juggled with time, advancing it here, retarding it there, and like an artist painting a picture, I heightened the lights, deepened the shadows in keeping with my instinctive conception of what the finished picture should be.

Curiously, although I invented Christian names for my wife and children, I never used my own Christian name or surname, or invented ones. I was the unnamed narrator.

In this second book I described in detail the restoration of the mansion, the clearing and reclamation of the land. I described how I achieved one of my life's ambitions by damming the stream to make a lake big enough for boating and swimming and ideal for the breeding and fattening of trout. Below the dam wall I installed a second-hand nine foot iron waterwheel, and geared this to a dynamo which gave us electric lighting for the mansion.

It was not however until the autumn that all the rooms in the house were reasonably fit for occupation and that we could start advertising my wife's nursery boarding-school. We had been joined by a Scarborough friend of ours, Sylvia Norman, who had been a visiting dancing and drama teacher at the Bradley's school, and was engaged to an R.A.F. officer, then in Egypt. She had brought with her a five-year-old niece, who'd had a narrow escape in a Scarborough air raid. There was room for two little official London evacuee girls and a lady whom I shall call Bertha, who had teaching experience, and had two children of her own, one a six-months-old baby. We had at least the nucleus of a school if the curriculum was not up to Board of Education standards.

Yet there was so much to educate and enchant the children in the place itself. There was an extraordinary resemblance between the pattern of the stream and the woods to those of our Yorkshire home. Both streams ran within a hundred yards of the house, with their source a hilly moor. Both were fringed with alder and stunted oak. And similarly, here was a natural playground where the stream could be dammed to make a shallow pool where there was clean sand, and an oak tree ideal for a swing. In so many ways, it was still the life we loved, the life of the Greenwood Tree.

How, and why, did things go wrong between us?

IV

ALTHOUGH I was older than my wife we were well mated. Our healthy family was evidence of that. We had, I'd always thought, a similar outlook on life, a love of the country and the sea, of unsophisticated people. We both found satisfaction and joy in making things, although naturally it was in the feminine arts like knitting and dressmaking, especially for the children, that she excelled.

Both of us had suffered from the force-feeding of religion in our childhood. We were agnostic, but tolerant to other people's beliefs, excluding Nazism, Fascism and Communism. We might I think have called ourselves Christian Humanists, for we accepted and practised to the best of our ability the kindly philosophy of the New Testament without its theistic and supernatural dogmas.

We'd been married at a Registry Office, without benefit of clergy. None of our children had been baptised. Our ideal education for them would be one in which they would get an unbiased instruction in all the religions and philosophies of the civilised world, and make their own choice—when they were old enough to do so.

We did not believe in hell, or the Day of Judgment, a prospect which had terrified me as a boy for I'd had a vivid picture of God on his throne with the Recording Angel reading out all my misdeeds, and The Devil standing by with a fork, eager to pitch me into the flames. I did not wish to have our children frightened in the same way. Nor did we think the deliberate building up by the Church of the agonies of Christ on the Cross, brought to a high pitch at Easter, a good thing for them. The main thing was that they should grow up to be kind, decent members of society.

Or was I kidding myself about my wife's complete concordance with my own views on religion, which had been coloured so much by the writings of Wells, Havelock Ellis, Bertrand Russell, the Huxleys, Gilbert Murray, Llewelyn Powys and Shaw; and by the Bible itself?

The ritual of the Church, the organ music, the singing of surpliced choir boys, the suave voices of robed priests, the magical phrasing of the Bible and The Book of Common Prayer, the beauty of the church itself, all brought to dramatic perfection on a Royal occasion, the funeral of a beloved sovereign, a coronation or the marriage of a princess, makes a strong emotional appeal to the female sex. Even the most hard-boiled atheist would be hard indeed not to be moved by such religious ceremonies. And we were not atheists.

Yet unless there is something in telepathy, it is true that two people can live in apparent harmony all their lives and yet never know precisely what is going on in the other's mind.

In the very act of an amorous embrace, a husband might be thinking about his last game of golf, or his football coupons, or his secretary's pretty legs (without any conscious adulterous intent). The wife might be thinking of a hat or a frock she has seen in a shop, or in the dark corners of her sub-conscious mind considering the comparative merits of arsenic and secconal as a method of taking her loved one's life and getting away with it, without of course consciously contemplating murder.

Our minds are private. We are all actors, masking our nasty thoughts and desires, pretending by our outward behaviour that we haven't got them. Only animals, and very young children, and primitive people are completely honest. And it is by our behaviour, what we do and say, that we can be judged.

I had no need to act the deep affection I had for my wife and children, although in the press of so many activities I may have been lax in expressing it in the way recommended in a

Reader's Digest uplift article on the art of preserving the early felicities of married life; that bouquet of her favourite flowers, that surprise box of chocolates reminding her of your courtship days, those little compliments and courtesies that mean so much to a woman! Maybe I took it for granted that she was always attractive to look at and didn't tell her so often enough. Anyway, she was curiously devoid of personal vanity.

Nor, in the three years of our stay at Castle Druid, did I ever have the least suspicion that her feelings towards me had changed. This may have been complacency, but it was not conceit. I had no illusions about my attractiveness, to her or any other woman. I was no Adonis. What had first drawn us to each other was this liking we had for the same sort of life, together with a physical compatability.

I was no saint, not even a Christian Humanist saint. I had, in my Flying Corps days, when the odds seemed all against any of us living a long life, done many of those things I ought not to have done. Even bishops when they intone the appropriate passage from the Book of Common Prayer make at least a formal confession of naughtiness. The fact that I paid no pathological penalty for my sins may have been due to my early training in the Army Medical Corps, which had included three months as an orderly in what was then known as a lock hospital.

I had never been an addict to drink, but many times in my life I had known what it was like to be gloriously tight. Fortunately, alcohol never made me quarrelsome. Nor did it stimulate my sexual desires. In the early stages of intoxication my behaviour was normal. I had the usual enhanced affability, a sense of feeling good. If there was music and feminine company I wanted to dance, for the sheer joy of dancing, not because I was in close contact with the body of an attractive female.

But when I got really tight I had an uncontrollable urge— and it must have been a throw-back to the jungle—to climb trees, to swing upside down, monkey fashion, from branches.

If there was no tree available, it might be a lamp-post or the rain-water fall pipe of a house. Once indeed I was mistaken for a cat burglar by a London bobby, and I was frisked for jemmies and weapons. This was after a bottle party given by Barbara Hepworth and her husband Jack Skeaping and Henry (then Harry) Moore.

I'd sleep like a top after such a night, and instead of a head-achey, parched throat hangover, I'd awaken next day in fine fettle, with only a hazy but pleasant memory of what had happened.

This was in my early bachelor days, however. You can't have bottle parties with a young family in the house. Besides, I couldn't afford the only drink I really liked the taste of—whisky. Yet as this book is going to be very much of a con-fession and a cautionary tale, I had better come clean about certain other traits in my character which—say in a divorce court—might be ammunition in the hands of opposing Counsel.

Although I was fastidious in never using the four-letter cuss word most popular among uninhibited males of all classes, and detested lavatory jokes, or for that matter the smutty story, I did consistently use bad language. I usually called a spade a bloody spade and, alas, often did this in the hearing of the children.

I had never quite overcome my boyhood antipathy to clergymen in general and country vicars in particular; although it is true that I could count several among my friends. For me, they, in their black clothes and silly collars, were the symbol of ultra-respectability, of narrow-mindedness and gloom. And why, just because they had studied at Oxford or Cambridge, or theological colleges, and passed out, should they be called Reverend?

Dynamite for hypothetical Counsel, who, but for the grace of God, might have been a vicar himself, and the judge a bishop!

It could also be said truthfully, but in a derogatory sense, that I had an "artistic temperament." Although for special occasions I did wear a suit and collar and tie, I usually dressed

23

rough; corduroy or flannel bags, an open-neck sweater, a sports jacket in winter. This was not affectation but a sensible garb for an active man, and if the garments got ragged and soiled it was evidence of my industry. I am blessed with a good crop of hair. This, at times, got a bit long and untidy if I was out in the wind, so that a stranger might mistake me for a tramp. Again, this was no affectation. It was just that I forgot or had no time to visit the barber.

But the term "artistic temperament" has a deeper implication. If I admitted it, and Counsel was familiar with the plays of Bernard Shaw, might he not quote that devastating speech of John Tanner's in *Man and Superman* in which the true nature of the artist is mercilessly exposed?

John is addressing the love-sick poet Octavius:

"The true artist will let his wife starve, his child go barefoot, his mother drudge for her living at seventy, sooner than work at anything but his art. To women he is half vivisector, half vampire. He gets into intimate relations with them to study them, to strip the mask of convention from them, to surprise their inmost secrets, knowing that they have the power to rouse his deepest creative energies, to rescue him from his cold reason, to make him see visions and dream dreams, to inspire him as he calls it. He persuades women that they may do this for their own purpose, whilst he really means them to do it for his. He steals the mother's milk and blackens it to make printer's ink to scoff at her and glorify ideal woman with. He pretends to spare her the pangs of child-bearing so that he may have for himself the tenderness and fostering that belong of right to her children. Since marriage began the great artist has been known as a bad husband. But he is worse; he is a child robber, a bloodsucker, a hypocrite and a cheat. Perish the race and wither a thousand women if only the sacrifice of them enable him to act Hamlet better, to paint a finer picture, to write a deeper poem, a greater play, a profounder philosophy . . . Of all

24

human struggles there is none so treacherous and remorseless as the struggle between the artist man and the mother woman. Which shall use up the other? That is the question. And it is all the deadlier because in your romanticist cant, they love one another. . . ."

I would have a defence to this. I was not a poet or a great writer. I had never felt resentful about the coming of the children. I had never been in the slightest degree jealous of them, a common enough trait in husbands and fathers of the stolidest nature, aesthetically dead as mutton.

But it is true that when I was engaged on the writing of a book and it wasn't going well, I might be moody, irritable, absent-minded, depressed, hungry for that sympathy, reassurance and encouragement that only a woman can give to a man; a thing that might well happen equally with any business man coming home after a worrying day at the office, to a wife who possibly was just as worried herself with personal problems.

It is also true that I needed complete quiet when I was writing, a freedom from any sort of distraction. A house full of children was not conducive to this, but at our Yorkshire home I had built for myself a wooden hut out of sound of the house where I could work in complete tranquillity; and, so that I should not be distracted by a view of the woods or the stream or the sea, all enticing me to more agreeable outdoor pursuits, I had put the window in the roof, studio fashion with frosted glass, so that even my sight of the sky was blurred.

Here in Wales I was not bothered about noise. To hell with writing! I'd leave that till after the war, when things got back to normal. I was now a carpenter—plumber—bricklayer, a house decorator, electrician, gardener and poultry keeper, and of course a farmer, and in some of these activities, notably the gardening, the house painting and the poultry, my wife, as well as running her school and sharing with the other women in the purely domestic jobs, was an enthusiastic and happy collaborator.

We had our tiffs. What couples, married seven years, haven't? It is significant that the thirteenth century originator of the Dunmow Flitch, Robert de Fitzwalter had specified "One year and a day" as the period in which the couple contesting for the prize of a flitch of bacon had neither quarrelled nor repented of their marriage. Anyway, in our first year at Castle Druid, everything went well.

Employing a contractor, we had ploughed, harrowed, fertilised and sown three of the once arable fields with oats, and successfully harvested a good crop. The school looked like being a success. I never expected that we would make money on it. But with several paying scholars, we were not losing much and our children were getting a more or less satisfactory education.

It was in our third year that the clouds of impending calamity began to gather.

My waterwheel, ancient though it was, had given me no trouble since we had first opened the sluice and set it going. A wheel of this type revolves slowly, making not more than eight revolutions a minute, for it is moving against the resistance of the gears, whose function is to multiply this speed to that of the dynamo drive. This apparatus I had contrived from bits of machinery from the quarry and a scrap-heap vintage motor bike.

The current for the dynamo was fed to storage batteries in the house, and when the batteries were low I would leave the sluice open all night. This I had done one night in the early spring. I was about to go to bed when I heard an awful noise coming, ominously, from the direction of the dam. It was very dark. I picked up an electric torch, dashed down to the dam wall, and, my heart in my mouth, shone the torch on to my darling wheel. It was a fantastic, horrifying sight.

The wheel was running free, and so fast that I couldn't see the spokes. It was also wobbling from side to side, and from one of the brass bearings came a stream of sparks like those from a blacksmith's anvil. The noise was unnerving, a pounding, clattering, shrieking hellish din, and the dam wall itself was vibrating under my feet as though battered by a ram.

There was a wooden shutter to the sluice which could be moved up and down between two vertical grooves. But it required both hands to raise or lower it. It was now raised of course. Trying to lower it with one hand, my torch in the other, it jammed.

I was now really scared, for if the wall gave way the whole lake would surge down the valley of the stream. Bridges, houses, might be washed away, people drowned. I dropped the torch and with both hands pulled frantically at the shutter. Suddenly it freed, I pushed it down hard. Then, with one final demoniacal shriek, the wheel stopped turning, and all was quiet.

I picked up the torch and moved down the sloping back of the dam wall to the wheel pit which was continuous with it. The machinery, the gears and the dynamo itself were unharmed. But one glance at the wheel itself told me that it would never function as a water wheel again. It was wrecked.

The teeth of the cast-iron spur were stripped. One of the spokes had come adrift and had been flaying the wall of the pit. Most of the others were loose and bent. One end of the axle had jumped its bearing, slewing the other end. It was this that had caused the cascade of sparks, the steel grinding the brass into a fine powder. And the most fantastic thing was that this powder had been sprayed like gold paint on to the structure of the wheel. A golden waterwheel forsooth!

So it was back to oil lamps and candles for the lighting of our house. I had at least got a title for one of the books I was going to write many years later!

V

"When sorrows come they come not in single spies but in battalions."

IN THAT same spring, our Scarborough friend, Sylvia, left us to get married. And as things were quiet on the north-east coast, she took her niece with her. She had been a wonderful help to us, teaching the children dancing, and producing little plays.

Two of our best paying pupils left at the end of the Easter term. There was a general feeling now that the big Nazi air raids were over. Soon, even our "official" London evacuees returned to their parental "fish and chip" homes, and apart from our own children, there were left only three scholars, one the four-year-old boy of the mother of two who had come to us in our first year.

From the first Bertha had lived with us on an informal partnership basis, making a financial contribution to cover the cost of food. Her husband was a scientist, engaged on some sort of hush-hush Governmental research, and he occasionally came for a week-end. We all got on very well together, although our views on certain fundamental subjects differed.

Bertha was conventional and something of a snob. She did not go to church, but she thought it right that one should have a religion, and really, if one was English, that religion should be Church of England. Practically all the best English public schools were C. of E. It was the religion of the better classes. Both her children had been baptised. Her own son had already been entered at a well-known public school.

Although Bertha preferred country to a town life—she was

enthusiastic about gardening and ponies—she had no interest in the "common people" of the country. I don't think that she approved of the way we had all our meals in the kitchen, with stools for seats, and Cornish ware mugs instead of cups and saucers, and no cloth on the scrubbed deal table.

Yet she was not aggressive in her views. She was a willing helper in the most menial of domestic chores. She was an excellent cook. All the children liked her. She was a good business woman too, and although I signed all the cheques, she kept the accounts for the school and the farm.

It was Bertha who, when we were discussing the falling off of pupils, our failure to get new ones, made the surprising suggestion that we might move from Castle Druid, and find a similar place either in England or at least nearer to the English border. It needn't be a farm, but just a mansion, and we could run it as a guest house as well as a school. There must be plenty of such places to let vacant, and there would bound to be enough land with them to keep poultry, and of course ponies. What was wrong with Castle Druid was its remoteness.

I did not take this suggestion seriously. It was unfortunate that the school looked like being a failure. But we had bought Castle Druid because it was a farm. We had, and at considerable expense, ploughed up and sown the remaining fields, sowing one of the fields we had cropped with oats last season with kale, so that we'd have fodder for at least two cows before autumn. We had also limed and spread ten tons of basic slag on the seven acre pasture that lay between the house and the stream, which should yield a good crop of hay. That alone, counting labour, and the necessary fencing, had cost nearly fifty pounds, but we'd have all that back when we got our cows and were selling milk to the Milk Marketing Board like the other farmers in the district.

Yes, I was asking for it! I was not a business man. Neither had I what it takes to be a farmer. Although Bertha kept the accounts I never disclosed to her my private finances. I rarely knew the exact state of them myself, and I got a jolt with a letter from my bank to say that my current account was overdrawn, and would I kindly make an adjustment from my deposit account, statement of which was enclosed. How icily polite bank managers can be when they have disagreeable information to impart to a client!

Fortunately, as we had sold our Yorkshire home, I was able to make this adjustment, for it was at this time that we had reluctantly decided to send our two daughters to a girls' boarding-school, not far from Carmarthen. (It was at least undenominational—and the fees were only sixty pounds a term). I was alarmed, however, to see that even the deposit account was considerably smaller than I had imagined.

Yet the meadow was looking good. The corn in the new fields was starting to sprout. And if when I went down to the lake, I purposely avoided looking at my wrecked water-wheel, I got a thrill when I saw the trout, some of them at least a pound in weight, and this in spite of the fact that with the water so clear they defied all my efforts to catch them with fly or worm.

And even the most expert and experienced farmer could not have foretold, or prevented, the calamity that now befell our newly cultivated fields. The blades of oats had sprouted healthily, and were growing apace. Then there appeared among them a reddish brown stain, as though they were prematurely ripening. As a gardener I knew that the stain was rust, a parasitic fungus, for which the only treatment is the ruthless burning of the infected plants and subsequent sterilisation of the soil. There would be no oats to harvest this year.

We were in a desperate fix. To her own unconcealed joy my wife now knew that she was going to have another baby. She had a passionate love for children, and had always wanted to have at least six. At any other time I might have shared her joy. But with the school, and now the farm a failure, I saw that the only way to stave off ultimate bankruptcy was for me to start writing again.

It was full summer, the wrong time of year for me to be writing, for I could not, like some writers, work outside; and to sit inside, with the sun shining was agony. And what should I write, anyway? I read through the first chapters of an abandoned novel, and put it down with revulsion. I read some of the glowing reviews of *Love in the Sun*, and felt even worse, for they were an ironic reminder of what might have been.

I think that under the circumstances I *would* have qualified for sainthood had I been able completely to conceal from my wife and the other members of the household that I was worried and depressed. I was an author in search of a book and the harder I concentrated, the more frustrating was my search.

"Artistic temperament"? I was gloomy, irritable, absent-minded. Indeed, if my wife had remarked to me at breakfast time that she and Bertha were thinking of going on a fortnight's holiday to London, still experiencing hit-and-run air raids, taking the children with them, I might not have answered at all, or said:

"Righto. I'll look up the trains."

But when she did tell me that Bertha had suggested a holiday I saw no reason whatever to object. Indeed I thought it an excellent idea. Bertha had a dated, and rather dilapidated Morris tourer. Her suggestion was that they should go to a little village up the Cardinganshire coast, which she knew fairly well, and stay at an inn or boarding-house. There would be sea bathing, fishing, and the children would just love it.

I thought it an excellent idea. The last of our pupils had left. It would be a good thing for my wife to have a complete rest. And without any distractions I was certain that within a fortnight I would get an idea for a book, and perhaps make a start on it.

And so they went, and I was alone in an empty, uncannily silent mansion. Two days later I got a picture postcard of a pretty little Welsh fishing village, with a message on it from my wife to say that all was well, and that they were having a very nice time. It was signed "With Love" and there was a postcript, "Don't forget to feed the hens and ducks."

There was no address, so that I couldn't write. This was a pity, for a day or two after, while I was sitting on the bank of the lake, looking at the trout, the idea of a book came to me. Not a novel, but a non-fiction book, a sort of *Compleat Angler*, in which I could describe the most exciting and amusing of my many fishing adventures, dating back to my first frustrating attempts as a boy to catch little rock fish with a bent pin for a hook.

I made a start the same evening, but I hadn't got far before I realised that I was not an expert angler. The fact that I couldn't catch the trout in my own lake proved that. I had never really used the dry-fly technique. I had never owned a really good fly rod. I had caught my biggest trout, a seven pounder, in a moorland mere not far from our Yorkshire home with the most primitive gear, and a fly I didn't even know the name of.

Yet there had been no period in my life in which fishing of some sort had not played a part; in England, in France, in Africa and Canada. It was one of the threads of my life. This book really should be an autobiography!

I had never worked so hard at writing as I did that week. I did remember to feed the hens and ducks, but for myself I subsisted on eggs, bacon and coffee, and I never stopped to wash up. I would do all this the day before the family returned, have everything clean and tidy for them, and I knew that my wife was going to be very excited when I showed her the pages of the new book and perhaps read them aloud to her and Bertha when the children were in bed.

At the end of that week I got a letter-card with the postmark indecipherable, not from my wife, but from Bertha. Obviously it was written hastily, probably on the counter of some village post office. It said briefly that they were touring round the country, that they were all well, and that my wife would be writing to me in a few days giving me all the news.

I was not really worried. Two days before the arranged
fortnight was up, and by then I had finished two long chapters
of the book, the postman brought me a small parcel, addressed
in my wife's own handwriting. It contained a quarter-pound
packet of tea, and a pair of my own socks, with holes in the
heels, beautifully darned. It also contained a four-page letter,
in my wife's authentic hand, and was headed care of the post
office at a town I shall not name. It began "My darling
Leo . . ."

It said that she was sorry that she had been such a long time
writing, and that she had to give me unpleasant news. She
only hoped that I wouldn't take it too badly. It was just that
she felt that she could not go on living our unconventional
and precarious life any longer. She had to think of the future
of the children. It was wrong for them not to be taught
religion. They should be brought up like other children, and
not like pagans. She wasn't just copying Bertha in saying this.
She had been thinking it for a long time, but knew I would
only argue to prove her wrong.

It wasn't my fault that the farm had proved a failure of
course, and it had certainly been rotten luck about *Love in the
Sun*, and she knew that I had worked hard at the house and
done my best about the school, but she had known that I
would have been furious if she had said that she agreed with
Bertha's suggestion of finding another place.

Well, they had found one, a much more suitable place than
Castle Druid, for it was nearer to England. Bertha had
already signed the lease, and they would move in as soon as
I sent the furniture, which she hoped I would do without raising
any difficulties. I could keep what I needed for myself, as she
supposed I would go on living at Castle Druid until I sold
it. She wasn't going to deprive me of the children of course.
She knew how fond I was of them and how fond they were of
me. Some arrangement would have to be made for seeing
them at intervals. But I must not try to see them at their new
home. She was going to have them all baptised, very soon,

and had already discussed this with the local vicar, who was a very kind, sympathetic man, with children of his own.

Again she hoped that I was not going to take this too badly. On the whole we'd had a very happy life together, particularly in our first Cornish home. In some ways it was a pity we had ever moved from there. The children would have loved it. But she had come to the conclusion that she would never live with me again.

And the letter was signed, "With Love."

No, I didn't stick to the facts in that Welsh book of mine. I used what any writer is entitled to do, my imagination, and wrote it as it *might* have been; and I called it *The Happy Ending*.

BOOK TWO

Paradise Creek

I

ARTHUR WELSH of the Fowey Polruan Ferry, landed me on the beach a hundred yards down the creek and out of sight of the cove. The tide was flowing, but it was neap, and it would be two hours before his deep-draughted motor boat could float into the cove. As I was in my best togs, Arthur, wearing deck boots, carried me piggy-back on to the shingle. He laughed when he set me down:

"Do you remember the way, or shall I come and show 'e? Must be getting on for more than twenty years since you was living here with your wife and kid. Why—I was a kid myself then, but I remember that ship's lifeboat you had with an old Kelvin engine. A proper job that! I used to come out here sometimes with my Uncle Bill, Stroppy they called him. He used to do odd jobs for 'e, between digging pits at the grave-yard. Couldn't 'e put the cider away! But there was no one could dig a pit as quick. Poor Stroppy is in the grave himself now, and it's my brother Puck who's dug the pits since the war ended."

Yes, I remembered Stroppy all right, and I remembered Arthur himself, then only a bright-eyed mischievous schoolboy, the youngest of eight virile brothers, his father a skilled ship-wright at Slade's Polruan Yard . . . But I was only half listening, as I had been all the way across the harbour from the station quay, for I was assailed with so many memories. Twenty years ago! Twenty years since that Christmas Day, when Ernie Slade of the then bankrupt and moribund yard had pulled me up the creek in his dinghy, and shown me the cove and the hut which was to be our home for the next three years.

37

"I think I can find the way, Arthur," I said ironically and with a conscious effort at calmness. "When can you fetch my things?"

"Don't 'e worry about that. I'll be here half an hour before high tide. And I'll fetch my little dinghy along. You can have her as long as you like. And I'll bring a can of paraffin, and milk and bread. If you like I'll ask my missus to come along this afternoon and give a hand. You'll find the old hut in a terrible mess. No one's been in it for years."

"Thanks, Arthur, but I think I can manage," I said.

He waded back to his boat, started the engine and sheered off into deep water, and I waited until he had disappeared round a bluff of the cliff on his way back to Fowey. I was alone, with no one in sight. I went down on my knees at the margin of the flowing tide and lapped up a mouthful of the crystal clear salt water, tasted the delicious tang and ceremoniously, as though I were drinking a toast, swallowed it. Then I walked along the beach until I saw the cove itself.

I had looked forward to this moment with excitement and a certain apprehension. Miraculously, for it was comparatively near to devastated Plymouth, the port of Fowey had escaped serious bombing during the war. But I knew that for some time prior to the Normandy landings, it had been a base for American assault craft. This would have meant shore installations, fuel and munition dumps, workshops, special jetties and slips. What, I had feared, could have been more likely than that the Americans had "taken over" the cove and adjoining land and in the urgency of their departure left it in a mess?

My fears were groundless. Here was the cove, unaltered and unharmed, as beautiful as I had ever seen it. It was not big. You could stride across its mouth in fifty paces, and in doing so you would be following the line of the rocky but tree-fringed south bank of the main creek, but from this line it receded abruptly for another fifty paces in the shape of a capital D with bare rock cliffs on either side diminishing in the centre to a narrow cleft, through which flowed a little stream. And to the left of the stream were two flights of stone steps, the beginning of the path which led up a short valley to the hut.

With mounting excitement I walked towards the steps. If everything went according to my plan, this was the beginning of the end of the unhappy state of affairs between myself and my family which had continued for so many years. I had tried many other plans. They had all failed. This one I felt was inspired.

The weather itself was inspiring. It was a morning in early April. The sun was shining. There was no wind. The air was warm, charged with the flavours and sounds of spring. There was a smell of warming earth, and primroses, and furze bloom and new grass, mingled with the smell of the sea. There was a twittering of finches from the tangle of furze and bramble that almost hid the little stream, and I heard the full-throated singing of a blackbird.

I climbed the steps which we had made ourselves, securing them with long iron bolts from the carcase of an old sailing ship rotting in the creek. On each side of the steps grew a profusion of long-stemmed primroses, undoubtedly the progeny of the roots we had transplanted from higher up the valley our first autumn. I walked up that familiar path, passing on my left the gnarled oak with its thick overhanging branch we had used for a swing for our first-born. And there ahead of me was the hut, at first glance in no way different to what I remembered.

I had been frankly told by the present owner of the hut and cove and eight acres of rough hilly land that went with it, that so far as he knew, the hut was not habitable. He was a retired army officer, who lived in Sussex. He had bought the property just before the war with the idea of using it as a holiday place for his family. But the war had interfered with his plans. His children were now grown up and married and he had been too busy even to come down and look at it. He did not wish to sell it, however. He was willing to let it at a nominal rent for as long a period as I liked, provided I would do any repairs or alterations at my own expense.

Was it habitable?

My biggest fear when I had first thought of coming back was that it was not only habitable, but that someone else was living in it. Even now I could scarcely believe my good fortune. But for the twittering of the finches, and the lusty singing of that blackbird, there was not a sound to disturb the quiet of the little valley.

I had the keys in my pocket. I decided that before going inside I would make an exterior circuit of the whole building. It was not, and never had been beautiful. It was a relic of the First World War, a standard army bunk-house, sectionally built of timber, sixty feet long and twenty feet wide and designed to provide accommodation for as many as two hundred soldiers. It had been transported, post-war, from an Australian camp on Salisbury Plain, and when we had first moved in there had been on its interior plywood walls the scribbled names and addresses, and also the *graffiti*, of many of its war-time occupants.

Slade's had bought it and re-erected it on its present site as a workshop. A large damaged sailing ship, too big for their Polruan slip, had been grounded in the cove for extensive repairs. Because of the narrowness and slope of the valley, the hut had been erected with its length parallel to the stream, and supported on piles at the end nearest to the cove. But the slope had been so steep that rather than have the end so high above the ground they had slanted the hut itself fore and aft. Our furniture such as table and beds and chairs had to be orientated to suit this gradient, fitted with unpaired legs. In walking across the hut one had to lean slightly to one side to maintain normal equilibrium.

I had come prepared for shocks. I got my first one when I reached the cove end of the hut, which had appeared unchanged, and looking underneath, saw that while the piles supporting the actual end walls were intact, several that had supported the

40

floor had rotted and collapsed, and the floor itself in places
was sagging almost to the ground.

Originally there had been two doors to the hut, one centrally
at each end. We had taken out the one at the cove end, re-
placing it with an eight by four feet window looking out on the
cove and creek, and putting the door in the side wall, with an
exterior wooden landing and staircase. Only one step of the
staircase had survived.

I carried on up the long side of the hut that faced the stream.
The stream had been one of our delights. We had cleared
it of weeds, made little waterfalls, with flower beds on both
sides, and just below the house we had dammed it to make
a pool. On the fringe of the pool we had planted two bamboo
shoots and we were thrilled when after many months we
found that the roots had "taken" with several new shoots
showing from the ground.

Now neither pool nor stream were visible. They were
hidden by a dense jungle of bamboo canes, some of them more
than twelve feet in height. Only by its gentle chuckling could
I tell the course of the stream.

But my present concern was the hut. Apart from the piles
and the steps there was nothing on this side to indicate any
serious dilapidation. The windows were intact, there was not
even a broken pane, and as I approached the end where the
piles were shorter, even the floor seemed to be all right. It was
not until I passed round the far end of the hut, and forced my
way through the bramble and thorn jungle of what had been
our vegetable garden, that I got a view of the whole building
and the roof and my second and more serious shock.

The roof was made of boards, covered with bituminous felt
secured, or at least meant to be secured, at intervals with
battens. Most of these battens were broken and loose, the felt
torn, and in several places there was no felt at all, only the
bare board, which laid horizontally, would give little protection
against rain. But worse still the ridge of the roof which should
have had an even slant from one end to the other, had an

ominous dip in the middle, evidence that the rafters had given way.

Certainly my heart was beating faster as I inserted the key into the lock of the end door of my old home. With a squeak of rusty hinges, it opened, and I stepped inside, to be assailed at once by a strong fungus-like odour of dry rot. Yet my first visual impression was reassuring. The floor immediately inside the door was sound. The plywood ceiling showed no sign of leak: and the first room on the left side, which had been our bedroom, although its ceiling and window were festooned with cobwebs, seemed in good condition and habitable.

When we had first occupied the hut only one half of it had been converted into a dwelling-house, and that had been done simply with wood partitions, making three bedrooms and a living-room in which had been installed a small ship's cooking stove. There were no independent ceilings. At first we just whitewashed the rough boards of the roof and rafters, but later on we covered these with plywood. The bedrooms were right and left of the lobby that led to the back door, in which I now stood. The living-room took in the whole width of the hut, with a window on each side. The door into it was shut.

I looked into the room opposite to the bedroom which we had used as a nursery. Part of the ceiling was hanging down and the floor underneath it was dark and still wet from the leaking roof, although so far as I knew there had been no rain for several days. The distempered walls too were water stained.

The adjoining room was in a worse condition. The plywood of the ceiling had disintegrated and was hanging down in strips like tattered regimental flags in a church and the floor was damp and rotted through in several places.

I opened the living-room door. And now came the biggest shock of all. The wooden partition which divided this room from the other half of the hut had collapsed, bringing with it one of the main supports of the roof. There was a hole in the roof through which I could see the light of day. I had an un-interrupted view to the cove end of the hut whose wall was

42

indeed vertical, but several of the other roof supports were almost in a state of collapse, and at the sides the floor had left the walls and was contorted like the bottom of an empty cardboard box left out in the rain.

We had loved this living-room of ours, especially on a cold winter's night when the little stove was roaring at full blast and its top plate red-hot. We had, before our first winter, and long before the arrival of our first-born, made the roof watertight. With a providential cheque for a short story I had sold we had bought new linoleum for the floor. We had distempered the walls dove grey and hung them with gay pictures. We had made cupboards and shelves, installed a second-hand sink from a yacht for washing up, with a waste-pipe leading to a deep, closed-in pit in the vegetable garden. We had contrived two luxurious easy-chairs from motor car seats we had found on a dump, and it was in this room, sometimes working throughout the night, that I had written *Three Fevers*.

I looked at it now, and at the wreckage of the bigger room, with a sinking heart. The whole place was in much worse condition than when we had found it first. It would take months to make it even barely habitable, and if my plan was to succeed, I must certainly do more than that.

My wife, who with Bertha was running a pre-prep school in a mansion in the Cotswolds, had agreed that if I could acquire a decent house for myself, with modern conveniences, not too remote from shops and doctors, she would be willing to allow the children to come and stay with me for half of the summer holidays. She assumed that I would have some respectable woman as a housekeeper, at least while the children were with me, and although she did not specify "nearness to places of worship" among the desirable amenities of the "decent" house, it was to be a condition that I should not in any way influence the children's attitude to religion. They were being brought up in the faith of the Church of England and would be confirmed when the time came.

I might have argued that legally and morally I had the

right to have my children stay with me for a reasonable period every year, without any set conditions, that so far as religion was concerned it was an unwritten but generally accepted British law that they should be brought up in the faith of their male parent. But could my Christian Humanism be called a faith? Anyway by this time I had learnt the futility of argument.

Since we had parted, the wordage of the letters I had written to my wife would have made a good-sized novel. I had used every argument and plea I could think of to persuade her to change her mind—in vain. I had been humble, and I had been tough. I had sought the co-operation of mutual friends. I had suggested that we should both seek the advice of the Marriage Guidance Council, let them judge between us, and act according to their verdict. She had made no comment on that suggestion!

I had consulted doctors, psychiatrists, lawyers, and, needs must when the devil drives, I had even sought and obtained an audience with the bishop of the diocese in which she and Bertha and my family were residing before they had moved to the Cotswolds, and where the mass baptism had taken place. I thought that the bishop might have some persuasive influence over the latest acquisition to his flock!

He received me in a small, gloomy, comfortless room in his palace, which adjoined the historically famous cathedral. He was elderly, tall, rather thin and scraggy, and he was wearing the traditional black gaiters. He had a lean, deeply lined ascetic face, and he greeted me with a chilly unsmiling politeness. So that he should not think I was sailing under false colours I told him briefly what my religious views were, and that I was seeking his help on purely humanitarian grounds, to help me mend a broken marriage.

I had the impression while I was talking, that I might just as well be addressing one of the marble recumbent effigies of his medieval predecessors in office, whose tombs adorned the nave of his cathedral. There was not a gleam of sympathy in his steely eyes. When I had done he told me in so many words, that it was not in his province to take any personal action in such a case as this, but he would if I liked, before I went (the hint was obvious) join me in a short prayer. . . .

Yet I had never given up hope that one day my family would be united again. I had never believed that my wife's decision as expressed in that unhappy letter of hers was final. And in that letter was the inspiration of my present plan. She said that she had been happiest of all in our Cornish home, and what a pity it was in many ways that we had ever left it, for the children she was sure would have loved it.

"Softly, softly, catchee monkey!"

I had not told her of my plan, or given her the slightest hint that I was coming to Cornwall. I had written to her from an accommodation address to say that I was looking for a suitable house, and that I accepted her very reasonable conditions. She would get a surprise when shortly before the holidays I would tell her that I was back in our old home. And I would suggest to her that she herself might bring the children down, not of course to stay, but to see that everything was all right. She might bring with her our youngest son, now four years old, whom I had never seen. And she might, I dared to hope, when she saw the place, the cove, the hut, the garden, decide after all to call it a day.

What would she think if she could see it now?

The chimney pipe of our little stove was rusted through. I could see daylight where it penetrated the roof. The stove itself was warped and cracked, the hinges of the oven door broken. Some previous owner or tenant of the place (I gathered that there had been several since we had left it) had moved our sink from the vegetable garden side to the side opposite, and with an idiotic disregard for hygiene presumably led the waste pipe into the stream. The ceiling, the three still upright walls, all were damaged or decayed to some extent, owing to the leaking roof and consequent wetting. And even the living-room floor had a suspicious concavity suggesting that its supporting piles had rotted.

I was seized by a sudden despair. It was no use. Single-handed I could not possibly put the whole place to right in time for the summer holidays. Thousands of jobs would have to be done. If I worked day and night I couldn't do them all. And I would have to sleep. I would have to eat and cook meals, and also do my daily shopping.

The collapsed wall of the living-room, with its door, was lying in what we had called the big room, the other half of the hut. Although we had built a fireplace on one side, this room could never be satisfactorily heated in winter. It was thirty feet in length, twenty in width. It had no ceiling or floor covering. Our fireplace which we had built very solidly of stone and concrete, had been removed and in its place was a big hideous slow-combustion stove, the type actually used for these huts in war-time. It had fallen on its side, with its chimney pipe hanging loose from the wall, and this pipe too was rusted through, adding to the scene of desolation.

Unhappily I moved into the room, climbing over the fallen partition. The loose floor boards swayed and creaked under my feet but at the far end, where the piles had not given way, there was a tolerably level area, and I reached the window, with its view down to the cove and creek. I brushed the cobwebs from the panes with my bare hands, and looked. And what a view it was!

Although the town of Fowey and the harbour were just round the corner, there was not a house or any other sign of human habitation in sight. The high steep far bank of the creek was as nature had made it, with bracken and furze, now in full bloom, growing between the outcrops of bare rock, and here and there an oak.

The tide was still only three quarters to full. It was creeping slowly over the pale grey mud banks where gulls and oyster-catchers were taking their last pickings at the water's edge. And wading farther out in the shallows, its long spindly legs slowly moving *left—right . . . left—right* like a clockwork soldier, was a solitary heron, hunting flat-fish.

My spirits rose. Depressed by my examination of the hut, I had forgotten the beauty and enchantment of the creek. This *was* the place to live. This *was* a real paradise for children, especially in summer when the water was really warm, and they could paddle and bathe, and catch the fat delicious prawns which swam in on the flood-tide. There were cockles, and oysters too, to be picked when the tide was low, fascinating marine animals in pools and under stones. And there were fish. With the tide up the creek was a favoured feeding ground for flounders and plaice and bass and pollack. In early summer huge shoals of grey mullet would sometimes swim in on the flood, so that at high tide the whole creek would be packed with them.

And if the creek was not enough, the harbour was only round the corner, sophisticated Fowey with its yacht clubs, hotels, church and chapels, shops, cinema and shipping jetties on one side; the older, quainter village of Polruan with its boat-building yards on the other. And, outside the harbour mouth the open sea, and the cliffs and coves and sandy beaches of the coast.

Boats of course were indispensable. My landlord had told us that he had left a dinghy at Tom's Polruan boatyard, which I could have if I paid the storage dues. Impressed by an advertisement, I had already bought a sixteen-foot, part decked motor boat from a man who lived at the neighbouring port of Par. He was to sail it round to me as soon as I told him of my arrival. I had imagined the excitement of my children when I embarked them on this boat at the Fowey quay, started the engine, and set off on the trip across the harbour to the cove and home. She'd be big enough to carry them all, my wife too!

I turned away from the window to face reality; the heaving floor, the sagging, leaky roof, the rot and decay. But I was no longer disheartened by what I saw. I was not going to be beaten!

I'd been nearly penniless when we'd first found the hut. We'd been obliged to do all the job ourselves. Now I had a

47

bit of capital, not much, but enough to have put down the usual deposit on the mortgage purchase of a "decent" house had I been able to find one in post-war England. My landlord had made it clear that he could not compensate me for any repairs or improvements I might do to the hut. But he had given me security of tenure and an agreement not to increase the nominal rent of ten shillings a week no matter what I did to the place. Whatever I did spend would really be the equivalent of rent, if spread over several years.

In spite of everything I had seen, the hut was not beyond repair. The weather-boarded exterior walls were in fair condition. The floors could be jacked up on to new piles. The old planked roof with its felt covering could be stripped off, the rotted rafters replaced with new ones, to support a new roof of corrugated iron or aluminium. That would be an end to the leaks.

Obviously I could not do this myself. I would have to employ professional builders. And if I did that I might as well go the whole hog, and to hell with the cost. A modern cooking stove for the living-room, a sink with its waste pipe leading to a septic tank, and water laid on, piped and pumped from the spring which unfortunately was below the level of the house and the far side of the stream.

I was really excited now, visualising the whole place as it might be in time for the family's arrival. Because the floors had sagged, I had scarcely been aware of that original slant which had compelled us to give our furniture odd legs. This could be cured if we made the new piles higher. But it would be better still if instead of doing this, the hut was severed in the middle, one half of it raised to make it level, the other half lowered, and a short staircase built between them.

With the floor dead level, and the rafters hidden by a ceiling, and with an adequate system of heating, this big room with its entrancing view of the cove and creek could be made the real living-room. It was perhaps too big. If ten feet of it were partitioned off, a bathroom could be made on one side, an extra bedroom on the other with a passage between them leading to the staircase. And this would leave a room twenty feet square!

With labour and material it shouldn't cost more than three hundred pounds to do the main structural alterations. The smaller repairs, the fitting of new shelves and cupboards, the distempering of ceilings and walls, I could do myself. I had sold Castle Druid at a price that almost covered what we had paid for it, and spent on its reclamation. Half of this I had given to my wife, and I had also sent her most of our furniture, although she had insisted that I should keep certain pieces that we had made ourselves, including an arm-chair contrived from the discarded elm bellows of the Polruan blacksmith, Charley Toms.

These things, my books and gardener's and carpenter's tools, and other articles I had bought in anticipation of my setting up a home again, were now at the Fowey quay, waiting for Arthur and high tide. There was a bed and bedding, primus stoves, cooking utensils, crockery, everything I needed for personal use. I was prepared to rough it. But for my darlings, everything would be what the house agents call mod. con.

The whole place would be weatherproof and comfortable, and also labour saving. The stream was not big enough to power a dynamo, but I could install a small petrol engine electric lighting set for under fifty pounds. The sink and draining board would be stainless steel, with chromium plated taps for the hot and cold water.

The bathroom would be a dream. There would be lino on all floors, rugs and carpets, divans, easy-chairs, curtains for the windows (we hadn't thought these necessary in the old days) table-cloths, proper cutlery for meals. And although I still thought blue striped Cornish mugs and crockery would be most suitable and attractive in appearance for a family like ours, I would get a real china tea service with dainty cups and saucers, just in case, when the family were here, the vicar came to tea.

II

AFTER a late primus stove frying-pan breakfast I set off next morning for Polruan. The tide was down, but there was plenty of water in the lower reach of the creek, and I had taken the precaution of mooring the dinghy Arthur had lent me well out on a trip anchor, for she was too heavy to launch single-handed. I was dressed appropriately for the life I was going to live from now on, flannel bags, sweater, open-neck shirt and deck boots.

It was good to be in a boat again, to hear the lovely sound of rowlocks, to watch the curling rings made by the oar blades receding astern and merging into the rippling wake. This was the life!

I had resisted the temptation to dig some ragworms and make it a combined fishing trip. But I could not resist resting on the oars occasionally and peering over the side. It was another warm sunny day, dead calm, with the water clear as glass. The bottom was level mud, devoid of weed, yet marked with worm casts, the tracks of wandering shellfish and hunting crabs, and although I didn't see the fish I saw the mud clouds made by several small flounders or plaice as they scurried away from the boat.

Soon the creek widened and deepened into the main harbour. The whole of Fowey waterfront came in sight, from the ruined castle that marked the harbour mouth to the first of the up-harbour china clay loading jetties. The other jetties were hidden round a bend in the estuary of the River Fowey.

The town of Fowey had never held for me as much interest as Polruan. It was not, and never had been a fishing port. The old houses, or what the improvers had left of them, were grouped between the small ancient town hall, the more ancient but much restored parish church, and along a section of the waterfront. Some of them were typical "old world" two- or three-roomed cottages, built back to back or end to end with walls of puddled earth (called "cob") and roofs of slate. But among them were several substantial houses, the one-time homes of the port's wealthy merchants.

The rest of the town, built along the waterfront towards the castle and on the hillside above, was exclusively residential and comparatively modern. Here was the swank Fowey Hotel and several lesser hotels and boarding-houses which catered for summer visitors. There were terraces of private houses and large detached, ostentatious Victorian villas, but on the waterfront, where the ferry crossed to Polruan, was the creeper-clad Georgian mansion which had been the home of the famous "Q", Sir Arthur Quiller-Couch.

Yet I found nothing repellent in my present distant view of Fowey. Most of the houses and some of the villas had cemented and painted fronts, each with a different colour or tint. There were gleaming white, cream, pink, various shades of blue and green, and even turquoise. In the sunshine that was filtered by a diaphanous heat haze, it might have been some dreamy Mediterranean town I was looking at. Even the Fowey Hotel, at a range of a quarter of a mile, looked quite enchanting.

Had I been in Fowey however, looking across the harbour, I might have found the reverse view even more enchanting. There were no swank hotels or Victorian villas in Polruan. Its more numerous cottages and houses rising up the flanks of a steep hill from an ancient sea wall were tightly packed together, like those of my native Robin Hood's Bay. They were intersected with narrow winding alleys, and flights of cobbled steps. The roofs were grey sun-bleached slate, and again their fronts were painted in varying colours.

The alleys and flights of steps converged on a steep main street which led to the quay where the ferry landed. Close by were the two pubs, the Lugger and the Russell, and along the front were the ship- and boat-building yards.

The objects of my trip were practical and also sentimental. Arthur, on his return to the cove with my things, had given me much interesting information. There had been many changes at Polruan since those far-off days when we had left the hut to go back to Yorkshire. This had been in the time of the post Kaiser war depression, when more than three quarters of Britain's merchant fleet was laid up, when Cornwall's china clay industry was at a standstill, and practically the whole male population of Polruan was unemployed and living on the dole.

The Slades were already bankrupt, carrying on in possession of their idle yard only by the grace of their creditors. Charley Toms himself was on the dole. Then slowly the depression began to lift, rising eventually to the boom which preceded the beginnings of the Second World War. The boom came too late to save the firm of Slade's. The three brothers who owned it, Charley, Jimmy and Ernie were old men. Part of the yard was taken over by a firm of boat builders who had a yard up the river. The rest, a disused dock and a stone building adjoining the blacksmith's forge was leased to my old friend Charley Toms. With the financial backing of friends, a private company was formed. The dock had been filled in, and a slip made for the hauling up of fair-sized craft for repair. In addition new sheds had been built, equipped with power saws and planing machines. Charley Toms was now the port's principal yacht and small-boat builder, employing more than thirty craftsmen, including many of those who had worked for Slade's.

From what Arthur had told me, and from what I was now seeing for myself as I pulled towards Polruan, it didn't look as though the disastrous aftermath of the Kaiser's war was being repeated. Three large merchant ships were berthed at the visible up-harbour jetties, and two coasters were at the mooring buoys waiting their turn. The china clay industry was booming.

In Polruan, Arthur had said, there were at present no unemployed and wages had gone up too, in fact I might find
some difficulty in getting someone to take on the job of rebuild-
ing the hut. The only likely one was a bloke called Arthur
Bate who'd started up a building business with his four
brothers after they'd been demobbed from the services.

Not far from Charley's yard, which I was now approaching,
there was more dramatic evidence of the port's new prosperity.
Here, in my time, had been a disused pilchard canning factory.
Its buildings had been repaired and extended, and there were
two patent slips enclosed by a long concrete pier, which made
a sort of inner harbour. On one of the slips a coaster was
hauled up. There was the machine-gun-like rattle of pneumatic
riveters, the ultra-violet flashing of electric welders, and
everywhere were men at work. It was the Brazen Island Shipyard, owned by the Harbour Commissioners, built between the
wars for the repair of steel ships up to 600 tons but, Arthur
had told me, with plans to build new ships as soon as material
still in short supply became available.

I was tempted to pull ashore for a closer view, but I felt
that I was under a moral obligation to make my first call in
Polruan a personal one. Of the three Slade brothers, Charley
was dead, Jim was retired, and Ernie, the one I had always liked
best, was bedridden. He was living with his sister in a flat
above what had been his boat shed. My fear was that he might
be too ill to see me.

As I pulled in towards the quay the ferry launch, crowded
with men in their china clay dusted working clothes, was sheer-
ing off. Several of them were vaguely familiar to me, and
Arthur himself waved his hand and shouted:

"See you at dinner-time. Don't forget!"

And he must have told his passengers who I was for some
of them waved a friendly greeting. This was Cornwall. These
were the people I loved!

I pulled into the steps, got out, and walked up with the
painter in my hand, looking for a ring to make it fast. At once

a short, wizened, but extremely agile old man, also in clay dusted working clothes came up to me and stared. Then he grasped my hand and words gushed from him.

"Well, if it ain't Leo! Arthur Welsh told me you was back. 'Member me, Sharkie Tomlin? How're yer keepin'? How yer missus an' yer kids? My, I'm glad to see 'e back. That place yer lived in 'as got in a terrible mess since yer left it. But I reckons you an' your missus will soon have it nice again, with lovely flowers. I'm proper glad to see 'e back. 'Member that time the mackerel and the big pollack was in Coombe Bay, how we was haulin' 'em in fast as we could go, an' not a pollack under six pounds. Here, give us hold of your painter. I'll make she fast."

I remembered Sharkie. Although not a professional fisherman he was the acknowledged authority on all matters relating to the catching of fish in local waters, the best grounds under the prevailing conditions of season and weather and tide, information which he would willingly impart to anyone who shared his own enthusiasm. He fished from a green-painted fourteen-foot pram dinghy, as old, I imagined, as himself, and I saw it now tied up to the quay. He tied my own painter for me, and tactfully ignoring his inquiry about my wife, I said:

"How's the fishing now, Sharkie?"

He grasped my arms like the Ancient Mariner and his guest: and he spoke almost breathlessly.

"Not so bad. Not so bad. But listen, I'll tell 'e something an' you can believe it or not. You ever seen a pollack six feet long from head to tail? Nearly half the size of my dinghy? Now I'll tell 'e. Last back end this happened. A nice fine day, no wind, but a long easy southerly swell, and I was sculling round the Cannis Rock. Neap tide, just on the turn and getting on for dusk. I'd got a brand new hemp line, with four fathoms of twenty-pound nylon, and nice fresh ragworms. I'd got a few pollack, but nothing bigger than a couple of pounds. Then just as I was thinking of starting home I got a jerk that nearly pulled the line out of my hands.

54

"At first I thought I'd fouled the bottom. I stopped sculling and let the line slack, and then I feels 'im again, and I knew 'e was a proper monster. I tell 'e I've bin fishing 'ere ever since I was a lad. I've had some big 'uns, but never one like this. I held on to 'im, and believe it or not 'e was towing me, stern first like a tug-boat. I daren't try an' haul that varmint in. I had no gaff on board. Some lad had been playing in my pram and must have lost it overboard. I just hangs on, and lets 'im tow me, straight out to sea too.

"We must have gone a quarter mile, before 'e slacked off, and I dared to haul in a bit. Believe me or not, I was shaking from head to foot with excitement. An' I was praying too, to Almighty God. Please God don't let 'im get off. I begins to think God 'as heard me for I went on 'auling in, very slowly and gently, ready to slack off if 'e gives a sudden kick. I thinks to myself 'e's drowned 'imself with towing the boat and I've only got his dead weight. I gets to the swivel, and then the nylon line, an' just with the weight of him, that line was cutting into my hand like the wire a grocer uses for cutting cheese. But I goes on hauling, and praying too, and shaking, and I've only about a fathom of line left when I sees him, coming along 'andsome, not a kick in 'im. And what a monster. A pollack, all right, green back and silver belly, and I'll swear he was six feet from head to tail and must have weighed forty pounds.

"I knew that line wouldn't hold to lift 'im aboard. Even if it hadn't broken, it would have cut into my hand like a knife. Only thing was to bring 'im alongside, get my fingers in 'is gills and heave 'im in. I was shaking now as tho' I'd got the palsy. I hauls in another yard, maybe, and 'is head is within touching distance, 'is great mouth wide open, but 'is gills shut. I puts a turn of the line round a cleat, bends down with one hand ready waiting for the gill to open. I sees it open. I gets my fingers in, and as I does, that fish gives a great kick with 'is tail as if 'e'd bin a sperm whale, splashing water in my face so's I'm blind, an' when I can see, there's no fish, 'e's gone, 'an believe it or not, and I'm not ashamed to tell 'e, I sits down on the thwart

55

and I cries like a babby. Oh! what a fish! I'll never see one like that agin if I lives to be a hundred. . . . "

*   *   *

I had no recollection of meeting Ernie's sister in the old days. I found her a handsome, exceedingly affable woman in her late sixties. When I told her who I was, and that I would like to see her brother, if he was well enough to have a visitor, she ushered me into a well furnished parlour, and asked me to wait. The walls of the room were hung with paintings and framed photos of sailing ships, obviously those that Slade's had built in the past. There was a bookcase too in which, with a little alarm, I spotted a copy of my own book in which, without asking his permission I had conspicuously, although in no way unpleasantly, figured Ernie himself under such a thinly disguised name.

I was thinking of the possible implications of this when she returned, closing the door behind her. She said in a low voice:

"It's all right. He'll be very pleased to see you, very pleased. But he's getting on in years, remember. He spends most of his time sleeping, and don't be surprised if he drops off to sleep while you're talking to him. He did that when the vicar called to see him the other day."

I followed her into the bedroom, and there was my old friend, propped up on pillows in a bed drawn close up to the window which overlooked his one-time shipyard and the sunlit harbour, welcoming me with a smile, a twinkle in his blue eyes that gave an assurance that my book, if he had read it, had given him no offence.

He had changed of course. His hair was snow white. The hand that he reached out to mine was thin and shaky. But there were few lines on his face. His eyes were bright, his cheeks full and with colour in them, and without any teeth he looked more like a baby who had just been fed and bathed and put to bed than an old dying man!

Arthur had told me that he was getting near the end of his

tether. He had no disease. No pain. He was just "wore out."

It was unlikely that he was unaware of this. But there was no sign that it worried him. He asked me to sit down on the bed. He was very pleased, he said, that I had called to see him. Was it true what his sister had told him, that I had come back to live in the old hut? Why hadn't I brought my wife along too, and the little maid? But she must be quite a big girl by now, and he had heard that I had got quite a big family. A lovely place it was to live in up there in the creek, so quiet and peaceful, 'specially in springtime with the primroses and bluebells out . . .

I didn't wish to disillusion Ernie about my domestic affairs. I told him that I was here alone to get the place ready for my family to come down in the summer. Very likely by then he would be well enough to come and see us.

He chuckled.

"I'd dearly like to do that. I'm proper glad you've done so well for yourself since you went away. You must have made plenty of money, eh? More'n we ever made buildin' ships."

He chuckled again, and his eyes were twinkling.

"I read that book of yours you wrote about how you an' your young missus rented the hut an' the cove from we, and made a nice little home for yourselves. Can't remember the name of the book. But you was making a bit of a game about we, wasn't you? We had many a good laugh about that."

"You didn't mind then?"

"No. We didn't mind. 'Twasn't all true, but some of it was, 'specially about us all being so hard up, with trade being so bad. Things have changed here since then, eh? I looks out of the window and sees nothing but motor boats down in the yard where once we built real ships, schooners and the likes of they. But I ain't got no worries now about how we'm going to pay the bills, and the wages."

Ernie yawned. I remembered what his sister had told me about the vicar. He was looking, dreamily out of the window, but I saw his eyelids fluttering.

"Tez lovely, lying here and lookin' out, an' just doing nothing, tez lovely."

He yawned again, and his head sank slowly back on the pillows. His eyes closed. But there was still that smile on his face as he fell asleep.

I remained watching him for a while. It was a comfortable room, rugs on the floor, a fire in the grate, more pictures of sailing ships on the walls, a vase of anemones on the bedside table, everything spotlessly clean. But it was not luxurious, as it would have been if he had been rich. Dear Ernie. He had failed only because he lacked what it takes to be a successful business man. Like his two brothers he was a master craftsman, a shipwright and designer and builder of boats. He had taken a delight and a pride in his craftsmanship, and he was never to be hurried, even to please a wealthy and sometimes exasperated customer. A job had to be done right to satisfy himself first.

He was devoid of greed. He expected a fair reward for his skill and labour—no more. And above all he was kind, tender, generous, without spite or jealousy, fair minded, scrupulously honest and good humoured.

He was sleeping peacefully. "Half in love with easeful death," I thought as I pressed his pale thin hand resting on the counter-pane, and tiptoed out of the room.

* * *

My most vivid memory of Charley Toms was seeing him in his forge, with leather apron, his sleeves rolled up showing his thick arms, hammering a piece of white-hot iron on the anvil with mighty blows, then thrusting it back into the coals, and pumping away at the bellows until the flames and sparks rose up as from a miniature volcano.

From what Arthur had told me I was half afraid that I might find him now in his office sitting at a roll-topped desk, with an intercom. telephone and buzzer, wearing striped trousers, black jacket, collar and tie, horn-rimmed spectacles, dictating letters to a secretary. I had difficulty first of all in finding his office, for I had to climb over a maze of greasy wire cables and stacks of timber and between boats in various stages of repair, scraping, and painting to the old stone building that had once been a sail loft of Slade's, and then up a crazy staircase to a long room that seemed packed to the ceiling with coils of rope, chains, anchors, yacht masts, drums of paint and oil, canvas and other nautical gear.

There was, however, a relatively clear gangway on the left, and a closed door from behind which I heard an irate masculine voice. I could not distinguish what was being said. I waited a while, and when there was quiet, I knocked.

There was a shout, "Come in!" I opened the door. There were three men inside a room that would scarcely have accommodated a double bed. On the right was an office table with pigeon-holes stuffed with documents and there were more documents scattered on the table itself, at which sat a middle-aged man I did not recognise. On my left, standing up, with a telephone receiver to his ear was a younger man with a swarthy face and the figure of a heavyweight boxer. And between these two, sitting on an empty oil drum was the managing director himself.

"Hallo, Charley!" I said.

With a look of pleased surprise, he stood up. But before we had time to speak the big man was shouting angrily into the telephone. Charley took my arm and motioned me out of the room, shutting the door against the shouting.

"Well, I *am* pleased to see 'e," he said then. "I heard you was coming back. The gentleman who owns your bungalow wrote us a letter about that dinghy 'e left with us before the war, asking us to fix her up an' give her a coat of paint, but we'm too busy at present, I'm afraid, to do that."

"You're doing well, eh? Arthur Welsh told me you're now the biggest boat builders in the place."

Charley laughed.

"I'm not a boat builder exactly. I'm just the boss of the firm, or supposed to be. And the firm's not so big as Slade's

59

was in the old days, but we'm got some of Slade's best boat builders working for we. Times I wish I was back at 'e old anvil making an anchor or welding a chain plate for a yacht, and no hurry about it: no time sheets, and insurance stamps and income tax returns to keep you awake at night. Of course, my son Jack does most of the business of the firm. That's Jack on the telephone trying to find out what's happened to some engine been on order six months. And that's Bill Rawson at the desk. He's our accountant, but like the captain of a ship, if anything goes wrong I gets the blame. Come on, now. We'll take a stroll round the yard, an' leave 'em to it."

Certainly success had not made a tycoon of Charley. He hadn't changed much in appearance, except that he was wearing a suit and collar and tie, that his hands were clean and soft. He was still on the right side of seventy, not quite so tall as his son but as broad in the shoulders. He had a full, clean-shaven face and a jovial expression which with conventional white whiskers would have made him an ideal Santa Claus.

As he led the way down the steps and between the hauled-up boats he asked me about my family, and as with Ernie, I did not disillusion him. They were coming in the summer I said. He hoped I would bring them along to see the yard. It was clear that he was very proud of it.

Boats, ships of any sort, had always held for me an irresistible fascination. Here there were scores of them, most of them private pleasure craft, laid up for the winter and soon to be afloat again: open motor boats, cabin cruisers, racing and cruising auxiliary yachts, rowing boats and dinghys galore. Among them I assumed was my landlord's dinghy which he had given me, but Charley led straight on towards a large corrugated iron building with open doors through which I saw the bows of a newly-painted and obviously newly-built cabin crusier, and two other partly built craft.

"That's our main boat shed," Charley said proudly. "That cruiser's for a Birmingham gent who made a lot of money out of the war. Come's here in a Rolls Royce motor car. She'll cost

60

getting on for four thousand. But we'll not see much of that with material and labour costing what it does to-day. She'm a real luxury boat, chromium fittings, water closet, sponge rubber mattresses, power windlass, electric light, echo sounder, two forty horse-powered diesel engines, when she gets them. That's what Jack's been on the phone about. Come on, I'll show 'e."

Just then, however, there was shouting from the direction of the office, a relay of voices getting louder as a message was passed on from workman to workman like a bush telegraph:

"Mr. Toms, Mr. Toms—wanted at the office!"

Charley sighed.

"Drat it," he said. "You can't call your soul your own in this place. I'll have to leave 'e. But you have a look round the shed. Ask Sam Slade to show you that dinghy. 'E knows where it is. Maybe I'll see 'e later."

The genial but agitated managing director of the firm (and I was reminded of Ernie, peacefully asleep in his cosy bed with all his worries over) hurried away. I moved into the boat shed, my nostrils assailed by the delicious scent of pine wood shavings and sawdust.

Of all manual crafts there can be none more fascinating than the building of boats, from the laying of the keel to the riveting of the last copper nail.

The almost final stage, before the boat is covered with the necessary paint and varnish is to me more exciting than its first launching. With all its timber bare and the heads of the copper nails shining like coins, you can appreciate the craftsmanship that has gone into its design and construction, the curving planks, tapering from stem to stern, no two of them exactly alike, and yet exactly fitting to each other: the steam-bent wood ribs to which the planks are riveted and which give the hull its strength, the cunningly shaped "knees" which tie the gunwales and thwarts or decks together.

I glanced with admiration, but without envy, at the super cabin cruiser with its gleaming white enamelled hull and chromium fittings which was going to cost the Birmingham gent who had done so well out of the war four thousand pounds, and moved over to one of the unfinished boats where a middle-aged man and a youth were engaged in bending a long plank on to the half-covered hull. By his family likeness I guessed that the man was a Slade, but I waited until the plank was clamped home before I spoke to him.

It was Sam Slade, son of Jim, nephew of Ernie. He had the Slade slow, soft voice, the Slade smile and charm. We exchanged greetings. I told him that I had seen his uncle, and found him blissfully happy, that I had called on Charley, and that Charley had brought me along to have a look at the yard, and also to show me a dinghy, but that he'd just been called back to the office.

Sam grinned.

"Poor old Charley. He's got a lot on his mind. And so has Jack. The trouble is, the firm's got too many jobs on its hands, and Charley and Jack never have the strength of mind to refuse to take on more jobs. See that cabin cruiser, still waiting for her engines? There's another like her on order. This one here's a twenty-foot open launch for the Fowey pilots. T'other one's a half deck fishing boat for a retired army colonel over in Fowey. She'll have forty h.p. diesels. And the firm's got a contract for three naval pinnaces.

"All our shipwrights, engineers and painters are out in the yard to-day. Our foreman, Tom Lean and Fred Rickett are working on a yacht moored up river. Things are different from what they were when you were living up the creek, eh, and Slade's was bankrupt? We thought we were lucky if we got an order for a dinghy. If you wanted a new dinghy built now you'd have to wait a twelve-month. But I'll show you the dinghy you're asking about." He turned to the youth who had been helping him. "Go to the office and tell Jack we're running out of two-inch nails. But wait outside the office door if he's on the phone or he'll bite your head off."

He led the way to a shed close by. Like the one with the

office it was crammed with gear. The smell this time was the even more nostalgic one of tarred rope. In one corner, however, hidden by an old sail, was the unmistakable shape of a boat. I helped Sam remove the sail, and there was the dinghy.

I had an immediate shock. Although the boat was painted a hideous dark cabbage green, it seemed at first glance to be the very one we'd had built for us by Slade's when our own very ancient one which we had bought for a pound had literally split in two, a calamity which fortunately had coincided with the acceptance of *Three Fevers*. We had sold it when we had left for Yorkshire. Could it be the same? It was the same size, the same lovely shape. But ours, I suddenly remembered, had been clinker built, its planks overlapping. This was carvel, its planks flush.

"What do you make of her?" Sam remarked.

"She's a beauty," I said fervently. "Except that she's carvel she's the spit of the one Slade's built for us years ago."

He chuckled.

"She was built on the same moulds. There's never been better boat builders round here than my old dad and Ernie and Jim."

I was looking at her now with all the thrill of possession, falling in love with her, seeing her with that hideous paint burnt off, painted as we had painted our new dinghy, lifeboat blue outside, ivory inside with a red line along the gunwales. If only my wife was here with me now, I thought, to share my excitement! But I became practical.

"Is there much owing for storage?" I asked.

"You'll have to see the office about that. Charley won't overcharge, seeing it's for you. Do you want us to put her down? She'll be very slack with being laid up so long. She'd be full of water before you pulled her up to the cove. If you'll take my advice you'll burn off that old paint. Give her bottom a coat of anti-fouling and put her on one of our moorings, and let her fill and soak for a few days."

I saw the wisdom of this. But I was agog to make a start.

"Could you lend me a blowlamp, Sam? Where can I get the paint?"

He laughed at my eagerness.

"You'll have to see Charley about the paint, but I reckon all our blow lamps will be in use this morning until dinner-time, and it's not far off that now. And it looks as though Charley is still busy in the office, as the lad hasn't come back with the nails."

I was to meet Arthur at dinner-time, I reflected. I must restrain my impatience. Besides I didn't feel like making another call at the office in the present hectic circumstances. But I couldn't resist saying to Sam, who if his own father and uncles had been better business men, might have now been himself the boss:

"What do you feel about working here in Toms' yard, when Charley and Jack might have been working for you?"

He laughed:

"I've never thought of that. I'm happy as things are. I'd rather be building boats than stuck in an office. We get good wages. Charley and Jack are good chaps to work for. Things are all right. Now you come back after dinner-time. I'll get you a lamp and some paint, somehow or other. I'll be glad to see that dinghy afloat again. You could tell she was a Slade boat a mile off."

III

ARTHUR'S cottage was in a yard, reached by a covered alley from the main street. Its living-room was bright and cosy, with its window overlooking the harbour.

Arthur, who had just come up from the ferry, proudly introduced me to his young and very attractive wife, June, and to his two-year-old daughter Sonia, tethered in a high chair at the table, laid with a spotlessly white cloth and shining cutlery for dinner.

June had a mop of wavy red hair and the pale slightly freckled complexion that so often goes with it, and green-blue eyes. She was not Cornish. Her father was the chief officer of coastguards, a Hebridean from the Isle of Skye, where she had been born. Her voice had the musical lilt of the Highlands.

Arthur's face would have inspired any portrait painter or sculptor. In spite of his youth—he was still under thirty—it was full of character. He had a well-shaped head, with a broad forehead, a thinnish, slightly aquiline nose, high cheek bones, with slightly hollow cheeks, deeply tanned, a strong jaw, full lips with big teeth. His eyes, which were blue, were deeply sunk. Their expression was intelligent, frank, humorous, generous, but absolutely fearless. He was a man you felt you could trust in any emergency, and I was to discover that, especially during the summer months, his services during his spells off the ferry were in great demand for doing jobs connected with boats, grappling for lost moorings, careening a yacht on the beach for cleaning and painting, securing drifting craft in one of the summer south-westerly gales which coinciding with a spring tide produce pandemonium in Fowey's

65

usually so tranquil harbour. Although short, he was broad-shouldered, lean and muscular, incredibly strong.

Sonia had her mother's hair, but not such a vivid red. She had a smiling, happy, healthy baby face. Here, indeed, was a happy family!

Dinner was not quite ready, and as Arthur washed his hands at the sink, I asked him what had happened to him during the war.

"The time of my life!" he answered. "Five years' sight-seeing and all expenses paid by the Government. Not to mention a gratuity, and ten quid in lieu of a civvy suit when I was demobbed."

"It's a pity he didn't take the civvy suit instead of that ten pounds!" his wife said as she opened the oven door. "I can never persuade him to wear anything but his sailor's jersey even on a Sunday! He's got six service medals by the way." She added. "He won't wear them either, even on Armistice Day when everyone else dolls up and goes to Fowey Church."

Arthur laughed but he made no comment.

"You were in the Navy, were you?" I asked.

"No, but it amounted to the same thing. Royal Engineers. Inland Water Transport, launches and small craft. The time of my life. Egypt, Alex., Cairo. Saw the pyramids and the Sphinx. Handsome, I can tell 'e. Then Tobruk with a big shallow-water craft, carrying out our wounded every night to a destroyer. Then to Syria. A week's leave in Damascus. Handsome. Next year it was Sicily, Syracuse. You ought to see them Ity fishermen catching octopuses at night with a torch. Some lovely-shaped craft they've got. I wish my old Dad could have seen 'em. Next to it was Taranto, then Bari where I got the biggest fright of my life. We was only a few miles away when a Jerry plane hit a munition ship, with sixteen other munition ships close by and the whole lot went up. Talk about the atom bomb! Next it was Naples, with Vesuvius, only it wasn't in eruption, and the Isle of Capri, where Gracie Fields lives."

Gaily, his wife started to sing " The Isle of Capri" as she set down a steaming pie on the table. But Arthur went on: "It was back to Blighty after that, and a week's leave. That was when me and June started acourting. 'Member that time, June, we was in the Creek Woods, when a thunderstorm came on, and we had to shelter under the old hut. It didn't half rain, but we was dry and cosy. Wasn't we?"

"I know that I wasn't half scared to death with the lightning," she laughed. "Come on, Arthur, you serve the pie while I feed Sonia. I can't do everything." And to me. "I hope you like steak and kidney pie."

Arthur took charge, but he went on with his odyssey.

"I was up in Scotland next for a special course in diesels. Next it was Southampton, waiting for the Normandy invasion. But I didn't get across till a fortnight after the Landings. That's where I got my sergeant's stripes. After the big push, it was Belgium and Holland and then Germany and the Rhine. I tell 'e it was a proper Cook's tour, like you see advertised in the papers except that it was winter when we gets to Germany."

"Don't forget to tell him what happened in Germany," June put in dryly, "when you were supposed to be engaged to me. I suppose that was part of the Cook's tour, too."

We were all eating now. The pie was excellent.

Arthur winked at me.

"She means how I lost my stripes. Collaborating with the enemy! That was Duisburg. Boys will be boys, you know. Some of us were in a sort of café, having a sort of sing-song, like it might be in the Lugger or the Russell on a Saturday night. There were a few girls there of course, and naturally they was Jerries, but they didn't seem no different to the Dutch, or the English for that matter. Anyway right in the middle of it the white-caps come in, military police you know. And that was that. Court-martialled. Reduced to the ranks, back to sapper's pay. But the war was nearly over, and I was soon back in civvy street at my old job!"

I enjoyed that meal and expressed my appreciation of it to

June. I knew that both Arthur and his wife would have resented my offer to pay for it. Just as we had finished there was a knock at the door, and there walked in a tall broad-shouldered man in working clothes. Arthur introduced us. It was Arthur Bate, the builder.

June was just making a pot of tea, and she offered to give him a cup, but he politely refused, and he wouldn't sit down, he was here to talk business and had only a few minutes to spare. He knew the hut up the creek. What did I want doing to it? It just happened that he was finishing a job to-day, and had another starting in about a month, and he might be able to take the hut on if it could be done in that time.

I told him briefly what my plan was. Cutting the building in two. Raising one half, lowering the other. A new roof of corrugated iron, some new partitions, a bathroom and sink, a hot water system. The decorations I could do myself.

"I think we could manage that," he said. "But I'd want to have a look at the place first, of course. I tell you what I'll do. We've got a motor boat. I'll be up first thing in the morning, eight sharp. If it's O.K. we'll make a start right away. Sorry I can't stop now. I've got a bloke waiting to see me."

He went, and my other Arthur said:

"That's a bit of luck for you. He's a good chap, Arthur Bate, and so are all his brothers. All but the youngest, Pat, Baby they call him, were in the war. They'll do the job for 'e all right. And I've had a word with my brother Larrel. He's on the ferry with me. We'll come up Saturday afternoon, and get that garden cleared so's you can get some new potatoes, and beans and peas in it. It's not too late. I'm due back on the ferry in a few minutes. What are you doing this afternoon?"

I told him about the dinghy, that I was going to borrow a blowlamp, scrape it, then paint its bottom before having it launched to tighten up the seams.

"I can lend you a blowlamp, and paint brushes too, and a scraper. But keep that dinghy of mine as long as you like. Have your tea now, and then I must be off."

I was feeling good. Everything was going well. I was very impressed by the businesslike manner of Arthur Bate. If Larrel Welsh (I didn't remember him) was anything like his brother, they'd make short work of the garden. It would be grand to have our own potatoes and peas and runner beans, and lettuces when the family came. But best of all was that the hut would be re-roofed, the floors levelled, a bathroom made, a cooking stove and water supply installed, all within a month. Once that was done the rest would be simple!

IV

I SPENT the afternoon on the dinghy, burning off the paint, sandpapering the planks, painting up to the water-line with red anti-fouling, then up to the gunwales lifeboat blue. I didn't see Charley again, but Jack came along while I was at work and apologised for not speaking to me when I had first called at the office. There must have been a satisfactory outcome to his vehement telephone conversation, for his manner was extremely genial. With some trepidation, I asked him how much was owing for the storing of the dinghy. He told me that he had forgotten all about it, and wouldn't have known it was in the shed if the owner hadn't written about it. The charge for storing was a pound a year, but seeing this was for me, he'd call it a couple of quid!

The dinghy was in the water, on a mooring close to the yard, with the plug out and awash to her gunwales, when I got back to Polruan Quay, and my borrowed dinghy. But as I was casting off I saw Sharkie, again, hurrying along the quay waving to me. I waited for him.

"I'm glad I've caught 'e in time," he said. "This should be a good day for pollack. I'd 'av been out myself, but I've got to be on a night shift at the jetties. I've got a nice lot of worms in my pram I dug up last springs, an' they won't keep much longer. You take they. You try along under the lighthouse to Coombe, and if they're not there pull along to Cannis Rock where I hooked that monster I was telling 'e about."

It was the voice of the serpent! Deliberately I had not brought any fishing gear, or tried to get any bait this morning. I had too many things to think about and do. But I couldn't very well refuse Sharkie's offer.

"Have you got a line aboard?" he went on. "You can have mine if you 'aven't. It's there under the stern sheet along with they worms. I'd dearly like to be coming with 'e, but I might loose my job if I did. Take the gaff too. If you hook a big one you don't want to lose 'e, like that monster of mine."

I took the worms and the line and gaff, little thinking then what adventure they were to lead me into. I told Sharkie that I could not set off fishing now, as I was expecting a man from the Par with a motor boat I had bought, and hadn't yet seen. I'd perhaps have a try this evening.

"You couldn't do better than that. Best time of all for the big ones is dusk. Well, good luck to 'e. I 'opes you get a boat-load."

I was half-way back, and into the creek, when I saw a motor boat coming along at a good speed behind me. I stopped pulling. It drew nearer. It was painted white, with a one third deck, and there was a tall man steering. I had not much doubt now that it was the one I had bought. The man waved to me, slowed down and stopped abreast of me, and spoke my name, which I acknowledged.

"Well, here she is," he said. "Will you come on board? Give me your painter, and we'll take your dinghy in tow. How far up the creek do you live?"

His name was Fred. Alas, he is no longer alive, and so far as I know he has no surviving relatives, so there can be no harm in my saying that he had diddled me over that boat, although I didn't know it then. It was a slow process of discovery. The agreed price of it was £150, fifty pounds of which I had paid, the balance on delivery.

Fred was a man of many parts. He was about the same age as myself, and similarly he had been in the Royal Flying Corps in the early days of the Kaiser's war. In our correspondence about the boat he had told me that he was a fan of mine, and that it was through reading my book that he had come to Cornwall.

He was very good looking, tall, sparely built, with a charming voice. Between the wars he'd had some experience on the stage and in films, but he was by profession an electrical engineer, and in Hitler's war had been doing hush-hush work on radar. He had a passion for boats, however, not building them (he admitted that he had never mastered that highly skilled craft), but in repairing them, converting hulls such as ships' lifeboats, ex-naval pinnaces, into cabin cruisers or houseboats, buying these hulls cheap of course, and selling the finished product at a profit.

During the course of what proved to be a long and curiously happy acquaintanceship, he once told me that he had quite a gift for making an old boat look new, which, although he didn't quote it as an example, is precisely what he had done with mine. From his description and two photos I had assumed that it was an entirely new boat. All that was new was the topside for the deck, the deck itself and the paint.

He had been frank about the engine. It was converted from a 1928 Austin Seven motor car, with a reversing propeller taking the place of gear box, and an overhead sprocket and chain for starting. But even the engine was painted and looked surprisingly new.

"Starting's simplicity itself!" he remarked, as he gave the handle a quarter turn. The engine started. He pushed the propeller lever ahead, opened the throttle, and with the dinghy fast to a ring in the stern we moved up the creek, at what seemed to me a most impressive speed.

Falling in love with a boat is like any other sort of falling in love, you are temporarily blind to the defects of the object of your affection, and perceive only what is agreeable. As she had come abreast of the dinghy, I had noted her raked stem, the shape of her hull, her ample beam, her square stern, which was partly decked in. I didn't like her gleaming white paint. That needn't bother me for long. She would be lifeboat blue and white and red like my own dinghy. She needed a mast, if only to carry a flag, but she looked as though she might take some sort of sail, saving petrol in a following wind.

I was more than liking her. The tide was now full. We carried on up the creek past the cove. Then Fred throttled down until the engine was ticking over, stopped her with the magneto switch.

"She's all yours," he said. "Starting from cold, you simply choke the carburettor, flood her, give her one or two swings, propeller in neutral of course, and throttle slightly open, then one quick swing against compression. Now, as she's hot, she'll just start with a flick. You try."

I did so. The engine started. I put the lever ahead, opened the throttle. Then I took the wheel. Away she went.

"You wouldn't think that engine was nearly twenty years old, would you?" he asked. "She's doing over five knots at present and she's not full out. But would you mind turning round now, and dropping me at Fowey, as I've got to catch the bus back to Par. That is if you're satisfied with the boat."

It was an obvious hint. I had written a cheque for £100, and it was in my pocket. If I'd had any doubts I might have regarded his request to hurry back to Fowey and Par with suspicion. But I was satisfied. It didn't worry me that there was a considerable amount of water in the boat's bilge, visible through the narrow gaps in the bottom boards. Fred was now working the bilge pump, and, as though to anticipate criticism, he said:

"She's carvel built, you know, and this is the first time she's been in the water since I converted her. It will take a few days for her to tighten up."

It was a logical, if not a strictly accurate explanation.

I handed him the cheque. He was diddling me, of course. Although I didn't know it, I could have bought a reconditioned, converted Austin Seven engine for twenty pounds. I doubt if he had paid more than five pounds for the hull. Even the reversing propeller was second-hand. He was making at least seventy-five pounds clear profit out of the deal, allowing for his skill and labour, the planks of the topsides and deck, putty (there were liberal applications of this) and paint.

Yet I never regretted it. I never bore him any resentment. We had each got what we wanted. He was a charming man. I think that he knew that I knew he had diddled me. It made no difference to our friendship. I was very sorry when he left Cornwall. And very sad indeed when I heard that in an influenza epidemic he had died of pneumonia.

V

IT WAS after six o'clock when we parted on Fowey's Albert Quay, and the shops were closed. But I managed to get a meal at a café and then I returned to the boats. I had by this time thought of a name for my new love. I would call her *Amanda*.

I was feeling as excited as a schoolboy with a new bike as I cast off the painter. The engine was still warm and again it started at the first swing. I steered across the harbour.

Yet, as I'd had a meal there seemed to be no point in going home. I remembered the worms that Sharkie had given me. The weather was still fine, the sea smooth. Fred had generously included in the deal a two-gallon can of petrol. I could tie the dinghy to one of the ship mooring buoys and do what Sharkie had suggested, run out of the harbour to Coombe Bay and have a try for a pollack. That would give me a chance too to give *Amanda* a real try-out.

There was a convenient buoy near the mouth of the creek. I tied up the dinghy, having taken out the can of worms, the line and gaff. Then I steered for the harbour mouth, the engine running perfectly.

It was one of the pleasant customs of the users of Fowey harbour that if you passed another boat within a reasonable distance you gave a formal wave of your hand to its occupants, friend or stranger. It was a custom undoubtedly echoing from the earliest seafaring days when ships on lonely voyages might sight another, and provided it was not an enemy or a privateer, heave to, exchange greetings, news, perhaps provisions.

I passed the Fowey dredger at her moorings, and two men on her deck waved to me, and I waved back. The same thing happened with one of the two anchored tugs, but the occupants of a large swank motor yacht, two middle-aged men in yachting togs and a lady, did not as much as glance in my direction, although I passed within a length, and was prepared to wave to them. The ferry was alongside the Polruan quay and out of waving range.

As I approached the harbour mouth I throttled down, baited the line, and paid it out. Trolling was the accepted method for catching pollack or bass, slow or just drifting with live bait, faster with artificial. It was too early in the year for bass. I steered close in to the Fowey side, passing Ready Money Cove, with its sheltered sandy beach, which in full summer would be packed with holidaymakers. Above it rose the castle-surmounted cliff of St. Catherine's Point, which I soon rounded, opening up a view of the whole western coast as far as the distant Dodman's.

It was a lovely evening. The sun was lowering. The rugged cliffs of Gribbin Head in the middle distance were in shadow, but the tall red-and-white navigation tower on this was still sunlit, and I could just make out the tip of the Cannis Rock, a quarter of a mile seawards of the point, the place where Sharkie had hooked that Moby Dick of a pollack. The Cannis too was the scene of a memorable and terrifying adventure of ours in the old days.

We had been making a trip in our converted ship's lifeboat cabin cruiser, *Samaki*, a bigger boat than *Amanda*. With the weather very much as it was to-day, we had been tempted to round the Cannis and steam across St. Austell Bay to Meva-gissey. On our way back, a thick fog had drifted in from the sea, and quickly obliterated the coast-line. We had no compass, but luckily we sighted the Cannis Rock, then partly bared. The highest point of the rock was then marked by a wooden post.

But the headland itself was still invisible. I found it impossible to tell from the post or the shape of the rock whether we were north, south, east or west of it, and once we lost sight of the rock there would be nothing to tell where we were. I dropped anchor. There was no wind. But there was a gradually increasing ground swell, whose precise direction again I could not tell, although waves were breaking against the rock. There was nothing to do but wait. And it was three o'clock in the morning before the fog did lift suddenly, revealing the mainland, the lighthouse and lights of Fowey. I swore that I would never venture outside the harbour again without a compass.

I had no compass now, unless Fred had hidden one somewhere in the cabin, which I'd had no time to explore. But there was no risk of fog this evening. Even the heat mist that had made my aspect of Fowey so agreeable had dissipated. The sea was smooth and calm to the horizon.

I moved slowly along close into the cliff foot towards the first of the coastal coves, called Coombe. The water was deep, yet so clear that I could see the brown gently-waving fronds of the giant tangles, and here and there a patch of whiteish shingle. But I saw no fish. If there were any they were lurking under the cover of the sea-weed jungle.

I wasn't worried. I didn't care whether I caught a fish or not. I was entranced by the beauty of what I was seeing, the placid polished sea, on which strangely enough no other boats or ships were visible, by the shape and colour of the cliffs on whose ledges were scores of gulls, not nesting, but paired off, and courting, the males dancing about the indifferent-seeming females with up-raised quivering wings, and frenzied croaks and clucking, while in the air around them wheeled the jealous unmated males shrieking their rage.

I had forgotten the extraordinary beauty of these Cornish cliffs. They were composed of ancient sedimentary rocks which in the dim geological past had been subjected to stupendous lateral east-to-west pressure against the unyielding massif of the west Cornwall granite. They were folded and contorted into fantastic patterns, and in the reflected light of the sea they glowed with all the subtle iridescent tints of a pearl.

The engine was behaving well. The rudder had a tiller, and

I found it more convenient to sit on the stern deck and steer with the tiller instead of the midship wheel, one hand on the tiller, one holding the line. I kept my eye on the level of bilge. It had increased a little, but with a few strokes of the pump I soon reduced it. I opened the cove of Coombe. Here the precipitous Fowey cliff fell away to shore level, then rose again into a lower and less precipitous formation whose summit undulated towards the west, where it fell away again into the wider and more deeply indented bay and cove of Pridmouth, at present invisible. Half a mile inshore from Pridmouth, hidden by trees, was the Rashleigh Mansion of Menabilly which Daphne Du Maurier had used in the setting of her famous novel *Rebecca*. It was at the present time, I had learnt, deserted, but later on it was to become Daphne's own home.

As Sharkie had reminded me, Coombe was one of the best fishing marks within easy distance of the harbour. Once you had opened it you bore out seawards for about a quarter of a mile, turned and came back on the same bearing. I did this several times without getting a bite. If Coombe failed the usual procedure was to steer back to Fowey and try under the Polruan cliffs east towards Lantic Bay or, and this was more tempting as I was quarter of the way there, to go west for Pridmouth and Gribbin Head, and the well-remembered Cannis Rock. I could fish all the way there, and in this weather I might run into a shoal of mackerel, which would take worms as greedily as the conventional metal spinner.

The sun was getting low, but there was still nothing to indicate any change in the weather. I opened the throttle slightly and keeping farther out from the cliffs, steered for the Gribbin.

I had opened Pridmouth Bay, with its double sandy beaches fringed with tall dark pines, when I caught my first fish, a pollack so small that I threw it back into the sea. I tried the Bay itself in and out as I had done at Coombe, with no more success. I steered for the Cannis. The sun had set.

The tide was now ebbing, running to the west, with a slight

78

set out to sea, but being neap it was not strong. The post on the Cannis Rock which looming through the fog had given me some measure of security during the long frightening hours of our vigil had either been washed away in a winter storm, or perhaps had been deliberately removed, for a hundred yards seawards was a more conspicuous Trinity House anchored buoy which certainly had not been there at the time of our adventure.

I slowed down short of the rock, hauled in the line and put a fresh bait on the hook. I hadn't paid it all out before I got a sharp tug. It was a stout line, and I knew it was not a big enough fish to bother about playing it, but I put the rudder over to head away from the rock, saw that the gaff was handy, and hauled in until the fish was in sight. It was a pollack, round about four pounds in weight. With only the one line, and no spare hook, I took no risks, but gaffed it on board, rebaited, turned back for the rock and put the line over again.

I was fishing now, aware only subconsciously of the beauties of the scene, the panorama of sea and cliffs, the twilight glow in the western sky against which the conical mounds of the china clay pits on the hills beyond St. Austell were silhouetted like so many Egyptian pyramids.

Pollack, which are close cousins to the cod, are more coastal in their habits, preferring rocky bottom feeding grounds in winter, but feeding voraciously on the vast migratory shoals of sardines (which are immature pilchards) and herring fry when they can find them. They are very partial too to sand eels, and a live sand eel or an artificial substitute is a favourite bait. They never occur in such numbers as cod, and have little commercial importance. Their flesh, however, especially when they are feeding on sardines or herring, is of even better quality.

Pollack are wanderers and fairly gregarious. If you catch one, you may be fairly certain of getting another in the same place, and of going on getting more until they have moved on. I got another of similar weight straight away, and then thinking I had hit a shoal of them I stopped the engine and let the boat drift. I was within about two hundred yards of the rock.

79

My hunch was correct. There was no need now to pay out all the line. The fish were feeding not more than three fathoms from the surface, and almost as soon as the bait had reached this depth it was taken. I didn't catch the fish every time, and those I did were not so big as the first two. Indeed most of them I threw back. But it was exciting. I had no hope of catching Moby Dick but there was more than a chance of getting something big, now that dusk was falling.

The little fish were getting the bait however and before long I was down to my last worm. I decided to pack up, and use this bait for trolling on my way home. I put my hand on the engine. It was still warm. I took hold of the starting handle to give it a slow turn until I felt compression. But there was a surprising lack of resistance even when I turned it several times. Something was wrong!

I removed the engine cover, examined the starting gear, and saw with alarm that it was not engaging the crank shaft. A steel pin that should have projected from the shaft end must have loosened and dropped out. Without it the gear could not function.

There were several inches of bilge water under this end of the engine, but there was a gap in the flooring, and I felt for the missing pin with my hand, for the bilge was opaque with oil and tar. I was not successful. I'd have to pump the bilge dry. I moved to the pump, and while I pumped I noted that the boat had drifted seawards of the buoy and slightly to westwards of it. It was not dark yet, but the Fowey lighthouse was blinking.

It was a semi-rotary pump. You moved the handle backwards and forwards. I worked it vigorously, and in a surprisingly short time, it sucked dry. Yet the bilge was anything but dry. I primed the pump. It threw out the priming water, and that was all. Clearly it was choked. There must be some sort of obstruction in one of its four valves, which could be examined only by removing the bolted lid of the pump body.

The nuts of these bolts were fastened tight, needing a spanner to shift them. I searched the cabin for some such tool, but it was clear that Fred had assumed that I was well equipped with tools myself, and anyway that I wouldn't be so silly as to put to sea without thinking of possible emergencies. Dear Fred! I did find in the cabin a coil of rope and a block of iron, obviously intended for an anchor. I must, before I tried fishing for the crankshaft pin again, stop the boat's seaward drift. I bent the anchor to the rope, and gently, for it was certainly not a new rope, payed it out. It hadn't touched bottom however, before I reached the rope's free end, and bending this to the painter still failed to achieve anchorage.

I returned to my search for the pin. It might have been my imagination, but it seemed that the bilge was now deeper than when I had started pumping. It became certain that the pin had rolled under the engine itself, for I had felt every cranny of the nearby bottom. I gave it up, and took stock of what was not a perilous, but an awkward, embarrassing, and ludicrous situation.

It was not dark yet, but more lights were gleaming on the shore. The anchor was not touching bottom. The buoy was getting well astern, and now there was a perceptible puffing of wind from off land, helping my seaward drift.

And I was helpless. There were no oars in the boat. If I'd had a sail it would have been no good. I had no means whatever of propulsion, nor any means of arresting my slow but steady progress seawards. I might in time drift out of sight of land completely, into the shipping lane, be sighted by some wretched ship, probably a foreigner, who might want to take me aboard, claiming salvage, and abandon my boat, or radio my position to the shore, so that the Fowey lifeboat might come and "rescue" ⸺ ⸺ ⸺s with a dead calm, paper-boat sea!

A story for the newspapers too, or even the B.B.C., with possibly my wife hearing of it, and wondering how and why I had come to be in Cornwall. The cat would be out of the bag and no mistake. . . . What a blasted fool I had been in venturing out to sea in an unfamiliar boat, without taking the greenest landlubber's precautions!

Well, I must make the best of it. I was in no danger. If the bilge rose above the bottom boards I could bail out with Sharkie's empty bait tin, or use one of my deck boots as a bailer. I'd be damned if I'd do anything dramatic like soaking my shirt in petrol, setting fire to it as a signal of distress. The pity was that I had no bait left, except the single worm, or I could have spent the time fishing. I put this worm on the hook and threw it over. It was at once seized by a fish which I hauled in, another small pollack. I threw it back, and that was the end of the bait. I lit a cigarette, fortunately I had a full packet, and looked at the lights of Fowey, remembering my appointment with Arthur Bate in the morning, that all being well, he and his brothers would be starting on the hut straight away. Oh, what a blasted fool I was!

And then I heard the unmistakable sound of an engine from the direction of Fowey, and shortly, voices, one of them feminine. I struck a match and held it up. Then another. I gave a hail. I saw, dimly at first, a boat coming towards me. I hailed again, and got a strong masculine answer:

"Ahoy!"

The boat drew near. There was a tall broad-shouldered man wearing a felt hat at the tiller, two ladies, at least five teenage boys and girls.

It came alongside, and the helmsman said very affably:

"Hope we're not spoiling your fishing. I know who you are of course. I'm Wilfred Denaro, secretary of the Fowey Galant's Sailing Club. These ladies are friends of mine." He introduced me to them. But I was too embarrassed to catch their names. He went on: "I'd heard you'd come back to your old home up the creek, so I thought I'd come along and tell you about the club. We'd like to make you a member. But someone told us they'd seen you leaving the harbour. So we decided to chase you. Tell me if we're being a nuisance. Are you having any luck?"

I was not going to lose face if I could help it. I held up the two biggest of my fish, and said as though it was not of real importance:

"As a matter of fact I was packing up. No more bait. I've had some trouble with the starting gear of my engine. I wonder if you could give me a tow, that is if you're going back to Fowey?"

"Of course!" came the ready answer. "Give me your painter."

I hauled up the anchor, untied the painter from its end, and handed it to the affable and obliging Mr. Denaro. As he made it fast I asked him if he could lend me a shift spanner, but I refrained from telling him what I wanted it for. A spanner was handed over to me. The launch turned, with *Amanda* in tow, for home. There was just light enough for me to take off the lid of the pump, to remove from the valves the debris that had choked them, bolt the lid back and start pumping.

It was a near miracle. I'd be home in less than an hour and up early in the morning to meet Arthur Bate, instead of drifting miles out at sea, with even ultimate rescue and all its embarrassing implications problematical.

And my face had been saved. It would be dark when we reached the harbour. I would not have the humiliating experience of being towed past the quays of the town and Polruan with their interested observers.

Who was this Wilfred Denaro, whose face had been only vaguely recognisable in the dusk? I was to know him as the Good Samaritan of the present Fowey although a comparative newcomer to the port. Not rich but a philanthropist. A lover of children. A supporter of youth movements. Founder of the club, and not merely its secretary. A strict Roman Catholic, but broadminded. A Christian and a friend indeed.

VI

ALTHOUGH I found a joy and satisfaction in doing things with a house for myself, I knew my limitations, and found an almost equal pleasure in watching professionals do the job, provided they did it well. The Bate brothers were professionals, skilful, fast workers.

Arthur, the eldest, had been a sergeant-major R.E. in the war. He was the boss, but there was no bossiness in his manner. He was quiet, almost taciturn, but when he said a thing he meant it. The others were anything but taciturn. They argued among themselves, speaking their mixed Cornish and Services argot; liberally lacing their words and sentences, prefixing them, affixing them with that now famous four letter verb in its several grammatical and ungrammatical forms which had better not be printed: joking, laughing, and occasionally singing.

They were a jolly crowd. Russell, the second son, broader and heavier than Arthur, was the strong man of the team, although they were all fine physical specimens, and good-looking too: different, yet each with a subtle yet unmistakable likeness to each other. They were Jacks-of-all-trades, masons, carpenters, engineers, electricians, plumbers, who with the exception of Baby—Baby was the tallest of the family—had been caught up in the drag-net of war service, with all its risks of death and mutilation, and had survived unscathed.

Whatever their individual skills (Jim, the third son was a plumber who had been a gunner in the war, Pat a carpenter, Banter an electrician and engineer), they had no strict Trade Union rules and restrictions to bother about. The first job was one of demolition, stripping the layers of bituminous felt from one half of the hut, that covering the big room, removing the boarding on to which the felt had been nailed, and exposing the collapsed and broken rafters.

Arthur in his first survey had made an important discovery. The hut (these buildings had been mass produced) was built in portable sections bolted together when erected. This would simplify the job of cutting the whole building into halves, for one of the bolted wall joints came in the middle. He had also discovered that the floor too was built in independent movable sections, not even nailed on to the piles.

I watched the tearing off of the roofing felt without any sentimental regret, old acquaintance though it was. Bituminous felt is one of the many manufactured derivatives of petroleum. Laid carefully on smooth boarding like the roof of a chicken house, garden shed, or small garage, fixed with flat-headed nails at the overlaps, and further secured with wood battens, it is completely rainproof, and will last indefinitely without any painting. But the boarding of the hut roof was anything but smooth, which became increasingly apparent as the stripping continued. The superb craftsmanship of the ship and boat building firm of Slade's had slipped up badly. Or had they no heart in working on a thing already made, mass produced and without any beauty, slapping it up so that they could get on with the main job, the repair and refitting of the damaged sailing ship already berthed in the cove? The hut was to serve as a workshop, not a dwelling-house.

The boards were rough, of uneven length and thickness. Here and there there were gaps between them. No wonder that whenever there had been strong winds the felt had flapped, tearing itself loose from the nails and battens, letting the rain in: no wonder that in trying to patch the leaks with a strip of new felt I had made things even worse by driving some of the nails between the gaps of the boards and starting another tear.

There were places where there were at least four thicknesses of felt stuck together with tar. I remembered desperately trying this method of stopping a leak myself when nails failed, and one of the brothers remarked:

"There's enough of this —— stuff to —— well stretch from here to —— Land's End."

Some of the boards where the rafters had collapsed were rotted and broken, but most of them were miraculously sound. Among them were planks of oak, pitch pine, even mahogany. It was clear that Slade's had ransacked their yard for timber in their urgency. But timber even in the early years after the Kaiser's war had been relatively cheap. The brothers, who had started to prise off the boards as they were cleared, treated them with respect, and as one of the mahogany boards was removed, Arthur remarked to me:

"Do you know what you'd have to pay for a plank like that to-day? It would cost you at least a couple of quid. You're lucky getting all this stuff. There'll be enough to brace up all the rafters and mend the holes in the floors as well as to do the frames for the partitions. You're quids in!"

I had come to a mutually satisfactory arrangement with Arthur, after he had made his survey of the hut this morning. I had made it clear to him that my finances were limited, and that the place wasn't mine anyway. I was prepared to spend the sum of £350 which would have to cover the cost of material. I knew that stoves, baths, sinks, hand basins, etc., were now in short supply, and expensive because of what had become known as the Export Drive. We were paying for the cost of victory. I didn't want any makeshift plumbing, but if he could get me any of these essential furnishings second-hand I'd be thankful.

We had agreed that payment for work done would be weekly, and I would pay cash for material as bought. When the total expenditure looked like reaching the £350 mark he would show me the red light, and would not take it amiss if I called a halt.

Pleasant though it was to watch these men at work and listen to their salty talk I had my own jobs to think about and do. Until the whole of this half of the roof was stripped there was no need for consultation and I walked down to the cove to look at my darling boat and carry out a detailed examination of her which, if I had not made the deal by correspondence, I would certainly have done before agreeing to the price, although I would have found it hard to say no, if Fred had proved adamant.

I took with me a hammer and paint scraper.

The amiable Wilfred had towed me the whole way home last night, stopping only to collect my borrowed dinghy from the buoy, and I had beached *Amanda*. She was now high and dry on the shingle, leaning over on her starboard bilge keel so that I could examine the port side of her hull down to the keel. Deliberately I had not pumped her out last night and she contained a fair amount of water. If she had been completely empty it would have been proof of a very serious leak. As it was I saw several places, including two small nail holes, from which water was oozing or actually dropping.

From the water-line to the keel the hull was painted with black varnish, a refined quick-drying type of tar which is the cheapest, but a long way from being the best covering and preservative for the hull of a boat, and of no value at all unless painted on to bare and bone-dry wood. I scraped some of it off, discovered that it had been put on to a paint that might have been " anti-fouling," but it was too old to tell, and even this was on another coating. I scraped down to the bare wood.

Dear Fred! I remembered that the photos he had sent me had been slightly out of focus, a trick sometimes used by professional portrait photographers when the countenances of their subjects have lost the unlined fullness and smoothness of youth. I had no doubt that the hull of *Amanda* was very old.

There were, and I was examining one side only, two copper tacked lead patches near the keel, obviously fixed there to cover holes. Yet the wood where I scraped was sound. Tapping the planks with my hammer, like railwaymen tap the wheels of rolling stock, I found no sign of rot. With the help of one of the brothers who had come down with a load of discarded felt to burn it on the beach, I turned *Amanda* over on to the port bilge keels and examined the starboard side. There were no more patches but several dripping seams. It looked as though most of the leaks were at the seams, which as Fred had said, should tighten up in a few days.

But, thinking of the children, I daren't risk it. Although I hadn't yet got the measure of Fred's technique of making the old look like new it was clear that he had painted on the black varnish for show purposes only. It might be hiding other things than old paint. Again it was no protection against that most insidious of sea-water pests, a tiny crustacean called the gribble, which with the better known ship-worm, teredo, drills into and devours the hardest woods, destroying not only the timbers of ships and boats but the underwater supports of quays, piers, and bridges. The gribble is the marine equivalent of the furniture beetle. In sailing ship days, the only sure preventative against the ravages of both pests was to sheath the hull with copper. The modern way is to use a paint that contains a poison. Again that paint, known as anti-fouling, must be put on to the bare wood.

It meant that I should have to burn and scrape off every bit of the varnish and old paint, caulk and putty every seam and nail hole I might discover, and apply at least two coats of anti-fouling. Before doing this I would have to wait for the peak of the next spring tides, run her aground at high water, and wait at least three days before she was neaped, so that she would remain dry until the next springs.

Dear Fred indeed! With all the jobs that had to be done before the family arrived why had he sprung this one on me? I felt justifiably vexed, but it soon passed. She was a lovely boat. She'd look lovelier with her hull lifeboat blue, her topside and deck cream or light grey, with a red line along her gunwales. I'd be able to buy a short mast at Charley Toms's, fix it with a tabernacle on the deck with wire stays to the stem and on each side. There'd be a halyard so that I could hoist up a red ensign the day I went to collect the family.

I chocked her up with stones on to an even keel, got inside, took off the engine case and looked for the missing pin. It *had* rolled under the engine and I was able to fish it out with a bit of wire. I drove it into its hole in the crank-shaft-end, flooded the carburettor and gave the handle one swing. The engine started with an unsilenced roar. I stopped it at once. It was O.K.! I could use the boat as she was for my shopping until the spring tides. But then I would have my own dinghy, lighter than my borrowed one, and easier to pull. Yet even she would need another coat of anti-fouling, and painting above the water-line and inside. Another time consuming job!

I walked back to the hut. The brothers were sprawled on the ground, taking their ten o'clock break and refreshments from grub tins and thermos flasks. Arthur however stood up.

"Would you like a cup of tea and a bit of cake?" he asked.

I would have accepted gladly, for I'd had an early breakfast, but conscience forbade.

"Try him with a Cornish pasty!" One of the others laughed, and held a pasty up to me.

Again I declined. I just couldn't sponge on them for food, and after all I had milk and plenty of food in the kitchen, as well as my primus stoves.

"We'll have cleared the roof in another two hours," Arthur remarked, putting back the cork on his flask. "It won't take us long to get those rafters and the ridge braced up, and then we'll have to find the bolts holding the wall frames together at the half-way mark and get them out. I reckon there's a four-foot drop from one end of the hut to the other, so that we'll have to drop this half a couple of feet, and we'd better do that before we put on the new roof. But I'll measure up for the corrugated sheets, and bring them over to-morrow, as well as some concrete blocks to use instead of those wooden piles. What about the plumbing? Let's have a look at your spring. It's a pity it's below the hut level." He addressed his brothers: "Come on lads, get cracking."

There was a general return to work, but Arthur walked down with me to the spring.

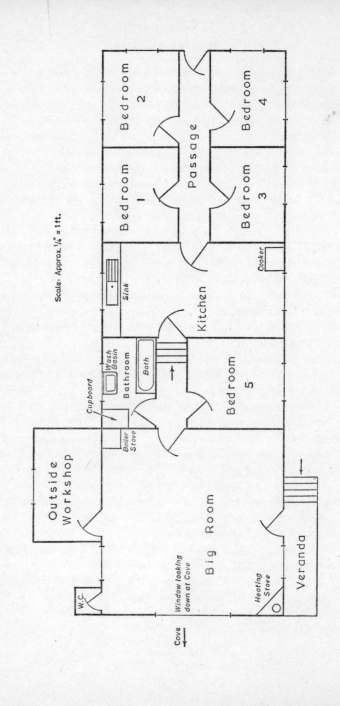

Scale: Approx. ¼" = 1ft.

We had never used the stream for domestic purposes as it was contaminated by cattle in the fields above the valley. The spring which had never varied in its flow, came out of the bank on the far side of the stream ten yards below the hut. Stroppy, Arthur Welsh's grave-digger uncle, had dug a deep pit just below it, and into this pit we had put two forty-gallon oil drums, puddling the earth round them. These drums, although rusted and half filled with soil, were still there, the water brimming over the top.

We had simply used them as a well, carrying our water to the hut in buckets. I must have something better than that now. Arthur clearly was thinking the same thing. For he said with an unexpected loquacity. "What you want for this is a motor pump. I think I know of one that would suit you to a T, if the chap who owns it hasn't sold it. A portable ship's emergency fire engine. War surplus. They had 'em on cargo ships for dealing with incendiaries. A Yankee $3\frac{1}{2}$ h.p. petrol engine with a centrifugal pump. It will lift up to forty feet and that's higher than the hut ridge. You'd just need a tank high enough to give a gravity feed to your bathroom and kitchen sink and pump the water into it. And damn it, you've already got a tank fixed above the privy. Let's have a look at it."

We went back to the hut, Arthur deliberately pacing the distance from the spring.

One of the owners or tenants of the hut subsequent to our leaving it had made an important contribution to its amenities by installing a toilet and septic tank. It adjoined, but was outside, the cove end of the house on the vegetable garden side and it was built of concrete blocks, used like bricks. The drain to the covered septic tank ran clear of the hut, but surmounting the building itself, and forming its roof was a huge galvanised iron tank designed to take rainwater from the hut gutter.

Arthur measured the height of the building, including the tank, and took a sight along the eave of the hut, and then said:

"Couldn't be better! If I can get that ship's pump, you're quids in. Only thing is we'll have to raise the height of the privy wall a couple of feet. Then you'll have a gravity feed to your bathroom and boiler and kitchen sink. And we can put a new drain alongside the hut to take your bathroom and kitchen waste to the septic tank. And while we're at it we might as well shift the door to the wall of the hut, so that you can get into the spot without going outside on a wet stormy night. You know, this is going to be a nice place when its finished. I wouldn't mind living in it myself! "

But he added, after a short pause, "In summer anyway."

VII

I WAS, as Arthur had said, "quids in." Next morning the fire engine, along with a quantity of corrugated-iron sheets and concrete blocks was unloaded from the launch and carried up to the hut.

"The bloke wants twelve quid for it," Arthur said laconically. "I took a chance and brought it along."

You don't fall in love with a stationary engine, like you do with a boat, or, for those who like such things, perhaps with a motor car. But I certainly liked the look of this one. The engine was a single cylinder, air-cooled four-stroke, the pump massively constructed of bronze. There was no means of trying the pump out at present, for it lacked the suction hose which on a ship would have gone over the side into the sea, but Arthur, who'd evidently had a demonstration of it from the "bloke," wrapped a cord round the pulley, gave it one pull and it started with a sound that suggested ample power for its job.

He let it run for a minute, then pressed a cut-out button on the magneto and it stopped. I was very impressed. It looked almost brand new and unused, and as I admired it I was struck with the thought that wars have certain compensations. If the German Kaiser hadn't started his war in 1914, there would have been no army hut for me to be living in now. And while indirectly at least Adolf Hitler was responsible for the break-up of our marriage—it was inconceivable that this would have happened had we not left our Yorkshire home—but for *his* war there would have been no anti-incendiary ship's fire engine going at a bargain price, to solve so admirably the problem of my domestic water supply. And bargain it undoubtedly was.

"I'll take it of course," I told Arthur.

93

"Right. Jim's our plumber. He'll fix it. But it's all hands this morning to get this end of the hut level. We've got four heavy jacks I've borrowed from Brazen Island Shipyard."

A jack, as every motorist who has changed a wheel of his car knows, is a mechanical device for lifting a heavy weight. I knew that it was going to be a very tricky job, this lowering of one half of a sixty- by twenty-foot building a distance of two feet. First it must be raised from those of the wood piles that hadn't collapsed; then the piles removed and replaced with concrete blocks laid on each other to the new level, and the burden transferred to them, but not in one sudden operation or the whole building would collapse.

It was fortunate that the floor was in movable sections. By lifting them up and stacking them at the cove end of the room (which hadn't to be raised at all), it meant that only the side walls, with the skeleton of the roof, had to be moved, and that the piles would be " getatable." Actually the whole structure could be regarded as a box, hinged at the bottom of the end wall, a box now raised two feet on this hinge, and which must be allowed to sink the same distance.

Before knocking-off time yesterday the roof had been stripped but for two rows of boards on each side of the ridge, left to brace the rafters together, and the broken rafters had been roughly but efficiently spliced. Their appearance didn't matter as eventually they would be hidden by the ceiling.

The search for the partition bolts, the lifting of the floor sections, had already started. I was too interested and excited to think or bother about my own jobs waiting to be done. I had to watch, and as with the lifting of the floor sections, give at least a token helping hand.

Arthur was silent again, thoughtful, evidently cogitating procedure, but the others were just as talkative, argumentive, and jolly as before. The finding of the first bolt was hailed with lurid acclamation, which became more lurid when the —— nut was found to be —— well rusted on to the —— bolt and would have to be cut with a —— hack-saw.

It wouldn't be necessary, Arthur decided, when the sections of the floor nearest to the dividing point had been moved, to lift those at the cove end. They were practically level. With his rule, a spirit level and a long straight-edged strip of wood, he got down to the earth foundations among the piles and began to make careful measurements. The floor sections had not rested directly on the piles but on five- by four-inch joists running parallel with the length of the hut. Although some of these, where the piles had rotted, had fallen, they appeared to be sound. Soon Arthur was calling for the concrete blocks.

These blocks were a by-product of the china clay industry of Cornwall. The pyramid-like mounds which are such a feature of the countryside around St. Austell are composed of coarse sand, the overburden of the deposits of clay, or kaolin, which itself derives from the geological decomposition of granite. The sand is mixed with cement and cast in moulds, in a standard size of eighteen by nine by six inches, so that laid on edge, each block is the equivalent of four standard bricks, quartering the time for building a wall.

Here however they were to be laid flat, a whole one on the foundation, then halves (one of the brothers was dexterously breaking them) piled on each other, without mortar to the required height as children pile bricks.

The ground itself, of dry crumbly soil, was uneven. Every pile must necessarily be of different height, to be checked with ruler, straight edge, and spirit level. The job would have beaten me, and I began to wonder if after all I had done the wise thing in having the whole place levelled, and not just put up with the slanting floors. It might indeed have amused the children to find their beds and the furniture with odd legs! But I had another very special reason for seeing it level.

Anyway, apart from a look of deep concentration on Arthur's face there was nothing to show that he was bothered or had any doubts about the success of the operation, and it wasn't long before the brothers working on the bolts announced that the last of the blank things were blanking well out. The whole team was now concentrating on the piles in the area exposed by the moved floor sections, removing those that were still standing, filling the holes, laying the foundation blocks of the new piles, but leaving the final adjustment of these to Arthur.

There were over thirty of them to be built and adjusted. When this was done, and by then it was nearly dinner-time, the joists were laid along them in level lines. But the two side walls were still on their original piles, only one of which, surprisingly, had rotted. And those walls, although unbolted from the other half of the hut, still had their slant.

It was not till after dinner (in my case coffee and a couple of boiled eggs) that the most dramatic phase of the operation began. The new piles had already been positioned under the walls, alongside the old ones, each higher than it would eventually be, yet low enough to allow for the insertion of the jacks. There were two jacks for each wall so that the lifts would be synchronised.

"It's going to be a slow job," Arthur warned me.

The jacks were in position, close up to where the building had been divided, a man to each, with Arthur in command. There was no joking, no wise-cracking now. Arthur gave a laconic order:

"Tighten up."

The mandrels of the jacks were turned. There was a creaking sound as the wooden walls felt the strain. Almost imperceptibly, they started to rise. Arthur had his hands on the nearest of the old wood piles. He exerted his strength against it, and in a minute or two, as the turning of the jacks continued, it loosened. He gave it a push and it fell. And his brother Russell, working the jack on the opposite wall, did the same with his nearest pile. In place of the fallen one, two new concrete piles were built, but shorter by an inch: and now Arthur gave the order to reverse the jacks. Slowly the walls sank until they were resting on the new piles. At this end they had lowered an inch below the level of the other half of the hut. Twenty-three inches to go!

Paradise Creek

It was a slow job. The process of raising and lowering had to be done along the length of both walls except at the end nearest the cove, then repeated with the concrete piles, the gain each time being only one inch. It was not strenuous. The jack is one of those simple mechanical devices which like a lever multiplies the effect of primary effort. But it called for skill, patience, confidence; and when, half an hour before knocking-off time the walls were lowered the final inch, leaving a vertical gap of two feet between them and the other still slanting half of the hut, there were shouts of "hooray" from all of us except Arthur, who just smiled modestly.

I shook his hand however and enthusiastically congratulated him and the team.

"But we haven't got the full effect yet," he said. "Come on, lads. There's just time to get the floor sections back."

I gave them a hand. Some of the sections had gaps where the boards had rotted, but the frames were all sound, and they fitted snugly on to the repositioned joists. The whole floor except for a slight slant at the cove end was level. Walking across it was like being on the deck of a ship, righted to an even keel from a list.

I was delighted: and not just because a level floor was going to add to the comforts and æsthetic amenities of my home. Among my possessions which Arthur Welsh had transported for me across the harbour from the railway station were three large and moderately heavy cardboard boxes still unpacked.

Some months before I'd thought of coming back to Cornwall I'd seen an advertisement in a local weekly newspaper, in the For Sale column. It described a model clockwork railway set, with more than 100 feet of sectional track, straight and curved. It included miniature stations, signals, points and switches, bridges, water tanks: four locomotives, two complete passenger trains, two goods trains, with dummy sacks of corn and packing cases, all accurate replicas of the real thing. The price was reasonable.

I was living then in a tiny bungalow in the Yorkshire Dales

P.C.   97   G in the biggest room of which there would have been space for six feet of track: but remembering how as a boy I had dreamed of owning any sort of model railway—all I'd ever owned was a wooden engine without any works—I'd bought the set.

Now, even with ten feet taken from its length at the kitchen end for the bathroom and another bedroom, there would be space here for all the track, sidings, bridges, signal boxes and accessories. There would be other toys, radio of course, and a gramophone. I was prepared for that contingency I dreaded most of all, a wet, cold August. Outside or inside, heat-wave or shivering rain, my family were going to have the summer holiday of their lives! I was hoping for the heat-wave all the same.

VIII

EVERYTHING was going well.

The raising of the other half of the hut presented no serious difficulties to the versatile brothers. Moreover it was done without stripping the roof of the old felt and boards, for the bedroom partitions had given support to the rafters, only two of which needed repair.

One of the disadvantages of a metal is that moisture condenses on its under surface in cold weather. It sweats. To obviate this, new felt had been laid along the rafters of the stripped half before the corrugated sheets had been nailed on. With the other half they had simply been nailed over the old felt, automatically curing the leaks and saving a great deal of labour at the sacrifice of the boards we might have saved.

Externally the appearance of the hut had been improved by the division and levelling, but it was still ugly and I rejoiced to find among the weeds in what had been the flower beds alongside and at the far end of the hut, several over-grown rambler roses. By next year I'd have them covering most of the external walls.

I didn't like the look of the corrugated iron roof either, but thought this a matter of small importance when, during the night following the nailing of the last sheet there was a sudden torrential rainstorm, which did not produce a single leak. Fortunately the storm was only a temporary break in the weather.

As the work of putting up the ceilings and the new partitions proceeded, I could not indulge in the luxury of watching it done. Nor had I any time for fishing. Arthur Welsh had kept his promise. He and his brother Larrel had cleared and dug over the whole of the vegetable garden, working Sunday as well as Saturday afternoon.

I liked Larrel. He was a year or two older than Arthur, with a pleasant, but less striking face, and he lacked Arthur's vivacity. His war service had been with the Navy, yet he was completely uncommunicative about his experiences. He was unmarried, and, I learnt from Arthur, spent most of his evening in the Lugger or the Russell playing dominoes and consuming a moderate amount of beer or cider, and occasionally getting pleasantly tight, and at all times ready to join in the singing.

I insisted against their protests on paying both of them for their labour, which included carrying up from the beach a huge quantity of sea-weed. With this for fertiliser I sowed a large patch of second early potatoes, which should be ready for lifting when the family arrived. I sowed peas, runner beans, lettuces, and planted two rows of tomato plants. In the garden were four apple trees, three pear trees, two Victoria plums, gooseberry bushes, black currant and raspberry canes, all neglected and overgrown yet showing signs of bearing some sort of crop. Certainly my children were going to be well provided for in the matter of garden produce!

I worked with a slow fever of excitement, thinking always of that day at the end of July or the beginning of August when I would go to the station to meet them.

I had got my dinghy. She was completely tight. I had painted her, inside and out, and fixed a thick rope round her gunwales as a fender, with a rope "pudding" at her stem. She looked very smart indeed. *Amanda* had been neaped, and dried out. I had burnt and scraped all the old paint off her, caulked all the seams, replaced the lead patches with new ones, extracted several rusted nails, and put copper nails in instead, clenching them to the timbers. With red anti-fouling up to the water line, and lifeboat blue above, she looked an entirely different craft.

But the finishing touch was the mast I had bought second-hand from Charley Toms, its butt housed on a thick block bolted to the deck, and wire stays fixed to the stem and to chain plates on either side. There was a pulley at the mast-top. I would have my red ensign ready for the day!

Jim had started work on the plumbing. I'd had another stroke of luck attributable indirectly to the late war, and Britain's Export Drive. I'd seen an advertisement in the Bargains by Post column of a daily paper announcing for sale a number of baths rejected for export on account of minor defects, the price eight pounds, carriage paid. I'd bought one. The only defects were a few chips off the enamel, which, using Fred's technique, I had doctored with paint. Hand-basin and sink I'd had to buy new, but Arthur Bate had found me a second-hand boiler and hot-water tank for five pounds, so that with a few lengths of galvanised pipe, to connect the pump with the big storage tank, the installation would be complete.

No other job or duty would have prevented me witnessing the final stage of this operation. I had cleaned out the accumulation of debris from both of the old oil drums at the spring, which had a pipe coupling them at their base. The fire engine had been fixed permanently alongside them, with a vertical four-foot rubber tube reaching to the bottom of the nearer one.

The pump had been primed. The engine started at the first pull at the cord. And almost at once the water in the drums began to lower, and Arthur Bate, who had climbed up to the now elevated tank on the toilet roof, gave what was for him a really excited shout.

"It's coming through like the bloody Niagara Falls. The tank's a quarter full already."

In a few minutes the boiler and the hot-water tank were full, and the water was running in the bathroom and kitchen sink tanks. I lit the boiler stove with odd bits of wood left from the carpentry. It burnt well. There would be hot water for the bath and sink whenever I wanted it.

For cooking I had acquired a brand new enamelled calor gas stove, with oven, grill, and two boiling rings. It was not so romantic as our ship's coal stove, but it absolved me of the possible charge that the place was lacking in mod. cons. Anyway the living-room would no longer be the kitchen, but the big room in which, thinking of winter, I would put in a modern heating stove.

Towards the end of the fourth week (and this had included a four-day break for Easter), all the carpentry, the partitions and ceilings were complete, and still Arthur hadn't given me the red light. The ceilings were of half-inch fibre board, their joints hidden by narrow wood battens. I knew from bitter experience that unless you gave these boards a coating of size, which is a weak solution of glue, painting them with any sort of paint is virtually impossible. They are as absorbent as a sponge. There were, I calculated, a total of 1,200 square feet of ceiling, and the sizing alone, a devil of a job, would have taken me weeks. The brothers did it for me, and the whitewashing too, before they packed up; and their final bill was still under my "red light" amount.

IX

AND NOW I was on my own again. With the holiday season getting into its stride, and the harbour starting to fill with pleasure craft, neither Arthur nor his brother could give me further help. The jobs still to be done seemed limitless.

How pleasant and innocent a garden can seem to the eye in the early stages of cultivation, when you have sown your seeds and raked the soil over, with not a green thing showing. Inspired by the coloured picture of the flower or the vegetable on the seed packet you have a pleasant vision of the little shoots breaking the soil in a few weeks' time and then advancing vigorously to maturity; forgetting that along with yours, nature has her own ideas of what plants shall be nourished by the soil you have prepared; nettles, docks, dandelions, buttercups, thistles, some of them so cunningly alike in their early stages to the ones you have sown that you hesitate to destroy them.

Forgetting too, that there are living things in the soil which may make a meal of your seeds before they germinate, that if they do break through, slugs, snails, mice, birds and an endless variety of other pests are marshalled for the assault: and one of nature's ironies is that weeds seem to be immune from all enemies except the gardener himself whose vigilance must never relax.

Fortunately my potatoes, apart from earthing up the first shoots to protect them from possible late frosts, needed little attention. But the peas, even the "dwarfs," had to be provided with twiggy hazel stakes, which I had to cut from a coppice on the hill above the hut: the runner beans needed a tall stake for each plant, and for these I hadn't to seek farther than my own bamboo thicket. Yet each stake had to be cut and trimmed, and the rows of them lashed together with horizontal bamboos to anchor the grown plants against possible summer storms.

Had I stuck rigidly to all the rules propounded by the experts in books, gardening journals and radio, the vegetable garden alone would have been a whole-time job. But outside the hut there were the flower beds. The paths had to be cleared. The one leading up the hill to the public path to Polruan was over two hundred yards in length and almost completely choked with thorn and bramble.

Inside the hut the walls of all the rooms had to be distempered, those with new partitions of fibre boards to be sized. The floors, although level and mended, were rough. To cover all of them with linoleum would cost a fortune. I had the bright idea of covering them with roofing felt, and painting this with red-tile coloured Liquid Linoleum, but I discovered the paint and the bitumen would not take to each other. Again my problem was solved, although it involved me in more hard work, by a Bargains By Post advertisement. Five gallon drums of War Disposal acetone paint, at thirty shillings a drum, carriage paid. It was dark blue. It exuded a nauseating vapour. But it dried almost instaneously, with a high gloss which made a perfect priming for the Liquid Linoleum.

With breaks only for meals, shopping and sleep I worked non-stop at garden or house, and already I felt justified in regarding it *as* a house, with its five bedrooms, well-equipped and labour-saving kitchen, bathroom with water h. and c., inside toilet, and its one huge reception room with its magnificent view of the cove and creek.

Whitsuntide came and went. There was still much to do. I had to paint all the windows, twelve of them, inside and out, a ticklish job. I had to paint the doors, again inside and out. The windows had no curtains: when I got curtains there would be the job of fixing rods for them. And as yet I had very little furniture.

Furniture in those early post-war years was virtually rationed. Newly married couples, provided they were lucky enough to find an empty house, cottage or flat, or even an unfurnished room, were permitted to buy such things regarded as essential for the making of a home. If they were well off, and not patriotically scrupulous about the Export Drive, there was the Black Market. But there were less rigid controls on the auction sale of second-hand furniture, and they favoured the buyer. A bedroom suite for example must not exceed a certain price. If there were several bids, then the bidders had to draw lots.

I didn't want any bedroom suites! I had started to make built-in wardrobes in all the bedrooms. But I needed chests of drawers, beds and bedding, carpets and rugs, crockery, including that china tea service, a settee, easy-chairs, all practicably unobtainable in the local shops.

An auction sale was advertised with a list of articles which included several of these desired items. They were the effects of a deceased lady, and others unnamed, and it was to be at a not too distant market town. I decided to take a day off and get there early.

Auction sales, unless you know precisely what you want and how much money you dare spend, are dangerous institutions. There is always the temptation to buy something cheap, just because it *is* cheap. And when you are bidding for something you really want it is hard to know when to stop and admit defeat.

I imagined that I was proof against the first temptation. I made no bid for a piano which must have cost at least a hundred pounds and was knocked down for five. But when no bid was forthcoming for a set of left-handed golf clubs in a bag (I was right-handed and didn't play golf), I was tempted to offer five shillings and got it. The beds and mattresses all looked like going to ceiling prices and I soon withdrew from competition. But I bought quite cheaply a dilapidated looking settee, two easy chairs with hideous upholstery which could be covered up, an antique oak dining-table with a broken leg that I could repair, and two deal chests of drawers which, although I knew I was letting myself in for more time-consuming jobs, I could transform with paint.

I paid a stiff price for a tea service which was to symbolise my surrender to convention. It would certainly look impressive on the dresser I was building in the kitchen. But I bought a whole batch of assorted plates and several mugs for ten shillings. I got a big handsome Chinese carpet, and several bedroom rugs for under twenty pounds. I resisted the temptation to bid for a stuffed badger in a glass case, which I thought might make an aquarium for the children, but I recklessly bid a pound for the contents of a large book case full of books, without being able to see what the books were.

But all morning I had my eyes on a Chinese cabinet, which was the only piece of furniture in the sale room with any real beauty. At lunch-time break I examined it closely. The cabinet proper was a yard in width, two feet high, and one foot in depth, and it fitted on to a five-legged carved stand. The exterior was dead black, decorated in gilt with human figures and geese. Its double doors opened to reveal eight drawers, their fronts enclosed with exquisite floral designs of mother-of-pearl. Inside the doors were Chinese landscapes, with trees, mountains and figures, again drawn and painted with masterly skill. Between the nests of drawers, however, were two narrow vertical doors, black and gilt when shut, but lacquered coral red and ornamented with storks and hornbills when opened to reveal a mirrored compartment, designed to hold a small figure of Buddha. There were little trays and compartments to hold incense and the various materials used in the ritual of devotion.

I was told by the auctioneer's clerk that there would be no ceiling on this item, which would be among the first to be sold when the sale restarted.

"If you have two loaves," runs the Chinese proverb, "sell one and buy a lily."

I was determined to buy that cabinet. With that and my

carpet, predominantly grey in colour contrasting with the tile red of the surrounds and various pictures and oriental pottery I possessed, and my settee and easy chairs suitably re-covered and book shelves along one wall, I would have at least one room that would be more than mod. con. even if it had also to serve for the model railway and a general play room in wet weather.

Fortunately there was still a vast number of items to be sold. The auctioneer was not a time waster. The cabinet was put up. Would anyone make him a first bid of twenty pounds? I was silent and tried to appear poker faced. There were no offers. He started a descending scale, and at last a voice behind me said "five pounds." I increased this to "six." The voice said "seven," and we went on bidding like a rally in tennis up to my opponent's bid of nineteen pounds. I called twenty. There was silence, then a hopefully hesitant "Twenty-one," I made it a determined "twenty-two." There was no response. The cabinet was mine, and I was so exultant that I bid for the next item, an enormous grandfather clock with hands and pendulum missing and described honestly as "out of order," and it was knocked down to me for thirty shillings.

X

AT THE END of June I wrote a carefully worded letter to my wife, telling her that I had come back to our old home.

I was particularly careful not to say anything that might make her suspect that my plan was to achieve a reconciliation: and just as careful to avoid giving her the impression that I was standing on my legal rights by asking her to let the children come to me for four weeks of the holidays. She had agreed to this anyway on her stated conditions, which I was prepared to accept. It was a reasonable condition that I should have a housekeeper.

A mutual Yorkshire friend of ours, Marie, was willing to come. She was a school teacher of unquestionable respectability, not straight-laced, but with views on religion firmly opposed to my own. She approved of children being baptised and being given early religious training. She had a jolly disposition however, a genuine love for the young which they instinctively reciprocated, and I was sure that my wife would give her approval.

"Softly, softly, catchee monkey!"

I was careful not to sound in any way exultant about what I had done to the hut. I referred to it as a hut and not a house. I certainly would have felt most unhappy if she and her companion had come here first and written to tell me how *they* had rebuilt and modernised it, a really dreadful thought. I did not mention my Chinese cabinet and carpet or the flower beds alongside the hut which I had cleared and sown with mixed annuals which would go on blooming throughout the summer.

I mentioned only the practical improvements, the levelling of the floors, the corrugated iron rainproof roof, the water supply, the "inside" toilet, the bathroom, the well-stocked vegetable garden. I had to mention the boats in case she thought there would be difficulty in getting a doctor if any of the children were ill.

They would be well looked after, I assured her. As she knew, the cove and creek were absolutely safe for bathing. Religion would be a barred subject so far as I was concerned. If any of them wanted to go to church or Sunday school they would be free to do so. And I ended the letter with the suggestion that if she had any doubts about its sincerity, she could bring the children (including our last born) herself, stay for a few days in a Fowey or Polruan hotel or boarding-house, visit the hut as often as she liked and satisfy her mind that all was right.

Throughout the years of our separation, I had acquired the facility of being able to tell at a glance if a letter from my wife contained pleasant or unpleasant information or a mixture of both. It would be like reading a review of one's newly published book which, starting with a few favourable remarks, might end with a devastating summing up, usually beginning with that horrible word *but*: or a letter from a magazine editor saying how much he had enjoyed reading the story you had so kindly submitted to him, which, regretfully, he found not quite suitable for publication. It was better to read the unpleasant information first and then take comfort from the pleasant even if it was only the sugar coating of the pill.

In her reply which but for the familiar hand might have been written by a stranger, she dispelled my hope that she would bring the children herself. The parents of several of her boarding scholars lived in troubled or unhealthy places abroad, and their children would be staying at the school for the holidays. She was short of staff, and she felt that Shawn, our last born whom I had not yet seen, was still too young to make the long journey to Cornwall, but perhaps he could come next year if I was still in the hut.

I swallowed that unsugared bitter pill and read the rest of the letter. She would send the other children. They should, she said, enjoy a holiday by the sea. She was glad that Marie would be there to look after them. She would send them three days before Bank Holiday to avoid the rush, and she trusted me to return them at the end of the four weeks as agreed.

Half a loaf is better than none, I thought, and this was more than half. My only serious anxiety now was the weather.

XI

So FAR it had been an average English summer. There had been spells of calm, dry, sunny weather like the one in April, that made one think that the sea could never be rough again, the sky overcast, with rain and chilly winds. There were spells when with the rain pelting down and the creek churned with whitecapped waves, it was harder still to believe that the rain would ever stop and the wind fall to a calm with the sky blue and the sun shining.

But it was a fine spell which came in the middle of July that caused me most anxiety. It was exactly the weather I wanted for August. Day after day the sun rose into a cloudless sky. What wind there was was off-shore and very light, the sea was not only calm, but the water warm, especially in the creek on the flood tide, so that swimming was a joy, or it would have been but for the thought that all this was too good to last.

I began to hate the very sight of the sun. No meteorologist, amateur or professional, had ever been able to predict with absolute certainty what the weather in any part of the British Isles would be like a week ahead. The only real certainty was its uncertainty. But the chances were against this July heatwave lasting. Each fine day increased the likelihood of cold and wet to come. If only it would rain and blow now! If only I could preserve this sunshine, the blue sky, the smooth warm water of the creek as you preserve summer fruits in bottles, keep it all for August.

I was obsessed with the idea that I must not enjoy these perfect days. They belonged to the children. The creek was full of prawns. I could not bring myself to catch them, although I had rigged up four prawning nets, a big one and three smaller ones. The mackerel and bass were in. So were the mullet. But the only fishing I allowed myself was to troll a line from the dinghy when I pulled to Fowey or Polruan for my shopping. I didn't use *Amanda* unless I had to make an urgent trip, for petrol was still rationed and I was building up a stock, but I ran the engine every day to be sure that it was in order for the Day. I had bought my Red Ensign, too.

The sun went on shining. I resigned myself to the probability that the break would come just before or actually on the Day, most likely with thunderstorms and torrential rain. Anyway, the main thing was that unless they caught measles or chicken-pox or whooping cough the children would be here. There would at least be some fine days in the four weeks of their stay when they could paddle or swim and catch their prawns and fish, when the sea would be calm enough to make trips in *Amanda* along the coast, land at one of the coves, make a fire of driftwood, picnic. And of course there was the model railway.

That first trip of mine in *Amanda* had been a warning. I had acquired a complete set of Austin Seven tools. I had made a sail out of a second-hand yacht jib I had bought from Charley Toms, and also fitted her with rowlocks and oars. I'd got a reliable compass, two anchors, plenty of new rope. I'd run no risks with the children on board, and no matter how fine the weather never venture more than three miles from the security of the harbour.

But with only four days to go, and the weather still showing no sign of a break, I decided to have a late evening's fishing. Big catches of mackerel and pollack were being made just outside the harbour mouth. It would be late before the tide flowed, however, and to make certain that *Amanda* would be afloat I took her on the ebb to a mooring buoy 200 yards down the creek. She would ground there on the mud at low tide and be afloat again before dusk.

Close to this buoy was another obsolete one, an iron cylinder about ten feet long and six in diameter, which with several holes in it had sunk into the mud for half its length. I saw it when I tied *Amanda* to the floating buoy, with at least three feet of water over its top, and I made sure that she was riding clear of it. I pulled back to the cove in the dinghy and pushed the dinghy well out in the creek on a trip anchor. *Amanda* was out of sight before I had reached the cove steps and for the next hour or so out of mind, for I still had many jobs to do inside the house.

I was in no hurry. The best time for fishing was dusk and a flowing tide. The sun had set, the flood tide was half-way up the creek when at last I walked down the cove, hopefully carrying an empty box and a tin of bait. I turned the corner of the cove, where the line to the dinghy was made fast. And then I had a fantastic and horrifying sight. From the level water of the creek *Amanda* was reared up as though surmounting a huge wave, her bow in the air, her stern within inches of the water itself, at an angle of forty-five degrees!

With my heart in my mouth, I dropped my box and bait tin on the shingle, hauled in the dinghy, got in and pulled with frenzied strength. A gentle breeze was blowing up the creek. Before I reached *Amanda* I'd realised what had happened. That breeze must have sprung up while the tide was still ebbing. It was gentle, and I would not have noticed it in the house, but it must have blown *Amanda* round against the tide so that her forepart had grounded on the sunken buoy, kept her there until she was fast. Her stern without support had lowered to the mud.

I reached her. My surmise was confirmed. I could see the sunken buoy, with about six inches of water covering its level top but not enough to touch the first two feet of the keel, still in the air, and there was less than two inches of dry between the rising tide and the stern. I looked inside. The engine box was dry, but there was water, and it wasn't bilge, covering the bottom boards astern of it. It was pouring through two holes in the transom which took the cables to the rudder. *She was near sinking*.

I looked desperately down-creek towards the harbour in the hope of getting assistance. There was no boat nearer than those moored in the harbour itself. All the pleasure boats which swarmed up the creek at high tide in the day-time must have packed up or be outside the harbour where the mackerel and pollack were shoaling.

I saw one slender hope for saving her. I got out of the dinghy, omitting in the extreme urgency of the moment to tie her, and stepped on to the sunken buoy. I saw that *Amanda's* keel was making only one contact with its edge about a yard from the bow. I grasped the stem with both hands, heaved. She moved, and I felt her keel grating on the edge of the buoy as she cleared. But as she did clear the bow instead of lowering went higher, her stern lower as the water poured in first over the stern and then over the gunwales. I hung on for a moment hoping that my weight might still bring the bow down and the stern up. The bow indeed did come down, but only to the level of the stern. Water gushed in over the gunwales over the whole length. With a horrible gurgling as the air in the cabin escaped she sank, and in the best tradition of the sea and ships, but unintentionally, I sank with her, holding on grimly to the painter ring of the deck in a last desperate effort to keep her afloat.

It was only a momentary immersion. The water was still only about five feet deep and not more than a foot over the deck. The mast of course was above water. She had sunk on an even keel. I stood up on the deck, shocked, unable yet to comprehend the catastrophe. Through the clear water I could see every detail of the boat, and it was almost incredible that it was submerged. The engine box had floated loose. Streams of bubbles were rising from the engine itself. I could see some of my tools lying on the nearby thwart. Then I saw that the dinghy was drifting away up creek and with it the engine box, *Amanda's* oars, and other flotsam. I kicked off from the deck, swam to the dinghy, picked up the box and the oars and pulled back, and by that time my mind had cleared and I'd got a plan of action.

No damage would be done to the boat by her sinking. It was the engine that would suffer perhaps irreparable harm. By morning the tide would have ebbed again. I could start bailing out as soon as the water in her had fallen below the level of the gunwales. When she was empty, the engine would have to be completely dismantled, every part cleaned with paraffin to remove the corrosive salt water, then dried and oiled. But if instead of waiting for the tide to ebb to where she had sunk I could get her near to the shore at high tide, I would be saving many precious hours. She would be partly buoyant. A powerful boat might tow her. I thought of Arthur.

There was no time to change into dry clothes. I was obsessed with a single purpose, to get *Amanda* going again in time for the children's arrival. It was a twenty minutes pull to Polruan. I was lucky. As I neared the quay I saw Arthur just mooring the big open launch in which he had first brought me to the cove. It belonged to the Ferry Company, but was used for transporting Polruan labourers to and from the china clay jetties, and for goods traffic. But this evening Arthur had evidently borrowed it for his personal use, for seeing me he held up a string of mackerel, and shouted:

"Would you like a couple for your supper? Grand sport just at the harbour mouth to-night!"

Briefly but urgently I told him what had happened.

"Give me your painter and come aboard," he said comfortingly. "And don't 'e worry. I've known engines sunk for weeks, and no worse for it when they've been cleaned up."

"But not converted motor car engines!"

"Maybe not. They're not built for boats. But don't 'e worry. Get she to bits quick and the salt water wiped off and she'll be no worse. Soak the magneto in fresh water and dry it out in the oven."

He had already cast off and started the engine.

"Of course," he added as he headed the boat up-creek. "Proper marine engines is the best. They'm built for the job, like the diesel in this boat." And as though he realised that this remark was not quite tactful, he said again, "Don't 'e worry."

We were there in five minutes. The tide was now half-way up *Amanda's* mast. I felt that Arthur knew his job, and I made no suggestions. The water was still clear. He edged the launch close until he could look straight down, and then he remarked:

"Is that a strong ring on her afterdeck?"

It was an iron ring, bolted through the planks, and I had three fathoms of stout rope tied to it for an emergency stern mooring.

"It's strong," I said.

"Handsome. If I can pick up that line we're O.K."

"I'll dive for it."

"No need for that, I hope."

He had seized a long boat hook. Dexterously he caught a loop of the rope, hauled it in, made it fast to a cleat.

He was giving orders now—like a ship's captain.

"Get your painter off the buoy!"

I nearly said "Aye, aye, sir," as I jumped into the dinghy, and obeyed, bringing the end of the painter from the floating buoy to the launch.

Arthur seized it, hauled it tight so that it was falling vertically to *Amanda's* stem. Then he handed it to me; and moved to the stern rope.

"Start heaving slowly," he ordered. "And keep step with me. We don't want to up-end her."

We heaved at our respective ropes. With the boat herself neutral there was only the weight of the engine and a small amount of ballast to lift. Slowly she rose. We went on heaving until the deck was almost level with the keel of the launch. It would not have been safe to bring her higher. And then Arthur shouted:

"Whoa. Far enough. Make fast!"

He peered over the side.

"Handsome. A proper job. It won't be high tide for two more hours, and I can't stop till then or June will play hell with me, and I'm due on the ferry at six in the morning. But we'll take her as far into the cove as she'll go so that she'll be on hard ground when she dries. Can you strip the engine yourself?"

We had started to move slowly towards the cove with the launch engine just ticking over.

"I think I can," I said hopefully. "It will only be a matter of unscrewing nuts and bolts, won't it?

He laughed.

"Yes. Like taking a watch to bits. It's putting the bits back in the right order where the trouble starts, unless you're an expert. I'd help you myself but the only engines I knows anything about are marine."

This sounded ominous. I was not an expert. I knew how an internal-combustion engine worked of course, the functions of carburettor, ignition and of the various moving parts, valves, pistons, connecting rods, crank and cam shafts. But I had never owned a car. I had never even watched the process of dismantling a car engine let alone seen one reassembled.

The tides were making, approaching springs, and we were well into the cove when *Amanda* touched bottom, with no more than a foot of water over her main deck. We cast off both ropes.

"Well, that's that," Arthur said. "Two hours and you'll be able to start bailing her out. I wish I could help, but you know what a wife's like about coming home late. I told her I'd only be out an hour. Eh—you'd better take a couple of mackerel!"

I took the mackerel. He refused my offer of payment for his services, but accepted five shilling as payment to the company for the use of the launch. I got into the dinghy, and he steamed off into the growing dusk, with a final cheerful shout:

"Don't 'e worry. Everything will be O.K.!"

XII

I DAREN'T go to bed. I changed into dry clothes, grilled one of the mackerel for supper, and began a restless vigil between the house and the cove. A watched kettle will not boil. It seemed hours before the tide reached high water mark and then as reluctantly started to go down. During this time I saw in my imagination the salt water already corroding and rusting the vital ferrous innards of the engine, the piston rings, the anti-friction bearings, the valves. I knew enough about electrical apparatus and its sensitivity to the wetness even of fresh water to have small hope that the magneto would survive this prolonged immersion.

Yet I could have enjoyed that night but for my anxiety. It never grew really dark for there was a waxing moon in the cloudless starry sky. The sea breeze had dropped to a dead calm, and breaking the utter silence of the creek I heard at intervals the splashing of big fish which may have been mackerel, bass, or pollack rampaging among the immense shoals of pilchard fry they had driven shorewards on the flood tide. I could have been among them in the dinghy, using my fly rod and a feather bait and there would have been no temptation to go to bed while the sport lasted. But I could think only of *Amanda* and my coming task.

Slowly, slowly, the tide went down. The water receded from the mast and then the foredeck and at last from the gunwales and the stern. The air was warm. I was wearing only drill shorts and shirt with plimsolls on my feet. I got into *Amanda* from the dinghy and with the water knee-deep I started bailing with a bucket.

The moon had sunk, the stars were dimming, and there was the glimmer of day in the eastern sky before I had reduced the water to the lowest part of the engine. There was light enough to see the nut and brass strap fixing the magneto. I removed it, carried it up to the house, stripped it to expose the coils and held it under the bathroom tap for several minutes. I wiped it dry. I had already lit the gas oven burner. I turned this off and put the magneto inside with the oven door half open.

Then, fortified with a mug of hot coffee I went back to the cove. Day was dawning. *Amanda* was high and dry. I pushed the dinghy out to deep water on a trip anchor. Then I chocked *Amanda* on to an even keel, climbed in and set to work.

Arthur's remark about taking a watch to pieces had impressed me. What boy hasn't done this with a watch or mechanical toy, and suffered defeat in the reverse process of putting it together again? The secret of success was method—not to be hurried, to place each part as removed on a tray or in a receptacle, and memorise or note the position and order in which it was removed.

I started with the resolution to stick to this admirable principle. I had brought three saucepans down from the house, and put them in a row on one of the thwarts. The biggest one I half filled with paraffin, so that I could clean each part removed. But the first job was to disconnect the exhaust pipe, the fuel pipe between tank and carburettor and then the water cooling pipe from the sea-cock (which I closed) to the cooling pump.

I had already discovered that the entire exterior of the engine and most of the interior of the boat was covered with an oily scum. The cap of the orifice in the crank case, through which lubricating oil was poured into the sump had come adrift, and the water, being heavier than oil, had pushed the oil out. Everything I touched was sticky with this scum. It was on my tools, and no matter how often I wiped them on an old shirt I had brought down from the house, it was on my hands, so that in exercising my full strength against the first nut of the manifold the spanner slipped and I lost a quarter of an inch of skin from a knuckle.

But I got the manifold successfully removed, complete with carburettor, revealing the square ports in the cylinder block. It would be easy to clean and dry the carburettor later. The manifold was simply an empty moulded iron tube. And now I had no guidance for procedure except the too obvious one of starting at the engine top and working downwards unscrewing every visible nut and taking off what could be taken off without undue force.

I was wrong of course. But at four o'clock in the morning who was to advise me?

The piece I removed first, and it was secured by nuts all tightly screwed, was the cylinder head. Between this and the cylinder block was a thin copper and asbestos perforated gasket to make a gas and water-cooling seal. The tops of the four pistons and of the eight valves were now visible. Two of the pistons were drawn into their cylinders, which were filled with water. All were wet.

So far I had made no vital error. I set to on the screw bolts securing the cylinder block to the crank case. At the cost only of a little more skin, I got them all out save the last. The faces of this were badly worn and none of my spanners would grip it. To add to my difficulty it was set back in a recess in the block close to the fly wheel.

The sun by this time had risen. It looked like being another exasperatingly perfect day, and now there were only two days to go before the children came. I was ravenously hungry, and starting to feel the strain of my night without sleep. I tried gripping the bolt with a pair of pliers. I lost a little more skin, but the bolt didn't move. I cursed it aloud, then laughed, remembering my resolve to refrain from swearing, in case I should do it in the hearing of my children.

Suddenly I thought of a possible solution. Somewhere among my tools was a small cold chisel. I wiped my hands on the saturated oily shirt and got out of *Amanda*, unfortunately knocking over one of my so methodically placed pans of nuts, bolts and washers, scattering them on the scummy bottom boards.

I walked up to the house, lit the gas, put on a pan of milk and began a search for the chisel. The milk had boiled over before I found it. But there was enough left for a mug of coffee which I gulped down with a piece of stale cake flavoured with the oil from my hands, before hurrying back to *Amanda*.

My idea was to cut the head of the bolt completely off. I gave it one oblique tap with the hammer and chisel however and it moved. It came away easily with the pliers. My hopes were rising. With the heavy cylinder block off I could unbolt the crank case from its timber bearings, disconnect it from the propeller shaft, lift it on to a thwart, drain out the sea water, clean and dry it inside, bolt it back and start the job of reassembly.

I had brought down what I thought was an old pair of pyjamas to use as rags. I wiped the scum off the block, seized it and heaved. It didn't budge.

I gave the flywheel a turn. Heaved again. This time the pistons moved, the water in the two flooded ones welling out as the others lowered. I poured some clean oil in them and gave the wheel a few more turns. Then I tried a direct lift, and the block moved and rose clear, the pistons, released from the cylinders, falling askew on their rods, looking absurdly like marionettes. Without an inkling that I had done something completely wrong I gave a shout of triumph:

"I've done it, hooray, I've done it!"

Everything now should be plain sailing. The pistons, connecting rods, cylinders, were all wet. The crank case was still full. But there was no sign of rust. The clearing of the crank case would be a simple matter. I had plenty of paraffin. Plenty of time too. It was still very early in the morning. If the magneto was all right, the engine might be running by the evening tide and *Amanda* afloat on her safe moorings, ready once more for The Day.

XIII

THE CRANK CASE was not so simple as it looked in my moment of exultation. Without much difficulty I disconnected it and lifted it on to the thwart. There was a draining plug to the sump and holding the whole contrivance over a bucket like a baby being held out on a pot I let the water run out.

But to get at the interior I had to remove the sump itself, a steel dish, deep at one end, shallow at the other, secured with at least a score of difficult bolts and washers. I had certainly got all the water out, but as I loosened the nuts there oozed from the sump a treacly sludge, covering my hands, dripping on to the thwart. I took the whole of my pyjama jacket to mop it up, and there must have been some irritant vapour in it for I had a sudden violent attack of sneezing. My nose was running and I had to wipe it on my shirt sleeve.

Still hiding the vitals of the case was a sheet of bronze gauze, secured with more bolts, and by this time I was not using the same care in parking the loose bits as I had done at the start. The sheet removed, however, I could get my hand inside, and by turning the flywheel wipe everything dry and repeat the operation with a rag soaked in paraffin.

The sun was sweating hot. My back was aching, my hands were bleeding in a dozen places, I was getting spasms of cramp in my legs, I was dizzy, and most damnably hungry, but come what may I had saved both boat and engine.

I climbed out, staggered up to the house, put on the kettle, washed my hands first with paraffin, then with soap, stuck plaster on my wounds and set about cooking a meal. The sight of the bones of my last night's mackerel on an unwashed plate did not tempt me to cook the other one, for mackerel although delicious have a distinct oily flavour, and temporarily I was off oil. Fortunately I had a tin of milk, and with more coffee, bacon and eggs, twenty minutes rest in a chair and a cigarette, I felt ready to get back to the job.

The crank case seemed dry. I squirted clean oil on the big ends, and the main bearings, bolted back the gauze and the sump, but with this I wasted many minutes looking for the bolts, some of which had dropped under the bottom boards. I lowered the crank case on to its bearers, coupled it to the propeller shaft, and fixed the bolts.

I had cleaned and oiled the cylinders. I was ready to lower the block back on to the pistons. I didn't of course know then what I know now. Each piston was furnished with three piston rings. These are made of spring steel cut diagonally so that their ends are pressed together by the walls of the cylinder and form a gas-proof seal. Free of the cylinder they project slightly from their grooves in the piston's surface but enough to bar entry unless the piston is pushed in dead straight.

A free piston can move in three ways, up and down and from side to side according to the position of the connecting rod; and again from side to side on an axle of its own called the gudgeon pin. The crank shaft to which the pistons are hinged by the connecting rods is so designed that the pistons are at varying heights in the cylinders so as to perform their functions in rotation. While two are going up two are coming down.

With bits of wood I had propped the connecting rods of all four pistons vertical. Numbers 1 and 3 were up, and Numbers 2 and 4 down. The block was heavy. Holding it in both hands I straddled the crank case and lowered the block on to Numbers 1 and 3. But at the moment of near contact the pistons were hidden by the block itself. At the first touch both pistons like wary butterflies evading capture moved aside.

I put the block down, propped the pistons vertical again and tried holding the block in such a way that my fingers projected and gripped the top of one of the pistons. But it was impossible to hold the block at the essentially horizontal level and at the same time coax the two pistons to enter the chamfered orifices of the cylinders deep enough to close the topmost rings. They moved in the wrong way at the slightest touch. They were animated, fiendishly malevolent.

I turned the flywheel so that all four pistons were at the same height and propped vertical, and tried again without success. My hands were trembling now with the strain of holding the heavy block. I got a severe spasm of cramp in one of my legs. I had to put the block down, and massage my leg with my oily hands.

It was no good. I was beaten. I'd have to give it up. I'd have to get an expert to do the job for me. Fred was the man. I had met him several times since the day he had delivered *Amanda*. True he had always seemed to have pressing business to attend to, but he had assured me that if ever I was in difficulty with the engine he would come and help. He had given me a phone number.

I went back to the house. It was now ten o'clock. I had no time to shave, but I made myself tolerably clean, and set off in the dinghy for Fowey which was a shorter pull than Polruan.

The real summer holiday had begun. Schools had broken up. The harbour was crowded with pleasure craft; yachts, cabin cruisers, sailing and pulling dinghys, dinghys with inboard engines, some with more noisy outboards. There were dozens of "drive yourself" motor boats mostly with happy-looking children among their passengers. Both the Town Quay where the pleasure boatmen plied for hire and the Albert Quay were crowded with visitors. And there were grown-ups and children on the private quay of the nearby Galant's Club, where I saw Wilfred Denaro superintending the lowering of a sailing dinghy into the water.

I had become a member of the club, but I'd had no time yet to join in its social activities. The building itself had been a boat builder's workshop. There was one large and lofty room, with settees and lounge chairs and benches round the walls:

french windows that opened to a veranda overlooking the harbour, and a smaller room with a tennis table and a refreshment bar where at any time members could make themselves tea. In the main room, which was bigger than the average Soho night club, there was a piano and radiogram with amplifier for the informal dances that were held every Saturday night to which Wilfred had given me a very pressing invitation.

But I was not going to presume on Wilfred's good nature in my present predicament. There was a telephone in the post office between the quay and the alley leading to the club. In the old days the Polruan postman had delivered our mail to the hut. But now the rural round was done in a van, and my mail came to the Fowey *post restante*. Only telegrams were delivered direct.

The phone box was occupied. I asked for my mail with apprehension, for my wife had not yet told me the time of the children's arrival, and there was still the dreadful possibility that for some reason or other they might not come at all.

But there was only one letter for me and it was from Marie. She would arrive at six o'clock. With a Yorkshirewoman's cautiousness she had made it a condition of her coming before the arrival of the children that she should "sleep out." She could trust me, but not the gossips, and she was running no risks. I had been able to get her a room at Polruan for to-morrow night.

The box was now vacant. I asked for the Par number Fred had given me. After several tries, the operator informed me there was no answer. I tried Charley Toms. Again there was no answer, and the operator told me that the firm was closed down till after Bank holiday. I tried the Brazen Island Shipyard. I might have guessed from the silence of the riveters as I pulled across, that this too was shut. There were two garages in Fowey, one specialising on marine work. These were open but neither of them had a mechanic who could be spared for any outside job at present.

I could not possibly ask Wilfred for his personal help for

such a dirty job. He was on holiday himself, blissfully happy among his club friends and teenagers. But he was the district sales manager of one of the big oil companies. He would know every garage and engineering shop in the district.

I rushed round to the club, I was just in time, for Wilfred was gathering a party for a trip in his launch.

"You're looking very worried," he said. "Anything wrong?"

I did not give him the details of my night's adventure. I'd got sea water into the cylinders and crank case and needed an engineer or someone familiar with Austin Seven engines. Did he know of anyone? The family was due to arrive in two days, and I'd be hamstrung without *Amanda*.

Wilfred who was Maltese by birth had a peculiar way of speaking: very rapidly, with the words tumbling over each other, and you might have the impression that he wasn't really listening to or interested in what you were saying. But you'd be wrong. His sympathy was always sincere, and if you had a problem his mind would be rapidly working on a solution of it.

"Jolly bad luck—jolly bad luck," he said. "You'll have to strip it down of course. Don't worry about the children. Let me know what train they arrive by and I'll run you all across to the creek. I'm looking forward to meeting them. Bring them to tea next Sunday, of course. There'll be lots of other children. You know Bob Shoebridge, don't you?"

I didn't know anyone by that name.

Wilfred went on:

"A delightful fellow, with a charming wife, too, Joyce. Just the very man for you. Bob's a potter, but he's got to read electric meters for a living. A born actor, too. He'd make his fortune on the stage or radio if only he could believe in his own talents."

I couldn't see yet how a potter, meter reader and potential stage or radio star however delightful he might be was going to solve my present urgent problem, but Wilfred continued:

"Bob owns a vintage Austin Seven car. You may have seen

it to-day on the Albert Quay. He's as proud of it as if it were a Bentley. A wonderful mechanic. Bob will help you. He's down in the boat yard now, painting a sailing dinghy he's built himself. Come on. I'll introduce you."

I followed Wilfred down a staircase from the veranda to the quay where a group of children were waiting for him to embark. Back from the quay was a yard and boat shed, and under the shed a youngish-looking man wearing sandals, shabby flannel bags and an open-neck shirt was kneeling by an upturned dinghy, a paint brush in his hand. He looked up as we approached and smiled, and in that smile I instinctively recognised a kindred spirit.

He was, I guessed, in his early thirties. He was of medium build, lean and muscular. He had an actor's face, not conventionally handsome, but with strong moulded features, a sharp nose, full mobile lips, expressive eyes: a sensitive face, full of character. But his manner was modest, almost self-deprecating. His smile was ironic when Wilfred, introducing us, called him a wizard mechanic.

"You mean," he said, "that I know how to read a meter!"

"That's Bob's modesty," Wilfred laughed. "I'll leave you to discuss Austin Sevens. Don't forget about my launch if your boat's not ready in time!"

He hurried off, leaving me a little embarrassed, for he hadn't told Bob what my trouble was. I made a tactful reference to his boat. He was still standing, paint brush in hand.

"Wilfred told me that you'd built this yourself. Do carry on. I don't want to disturb you."

It was an unusual type of craft, almost a flattie, yet cunningly moulded. There was a slot in the keel for a centre-board.

"Yes. I built her myself," he answered. "Not original design, of course. I just modified her from a pattern in a yachting paper. She sails well though. I'm just putting on the finishing touches to this coat. But what's this about Austin Seven?"

I didn't beat about the bush. Briefly I told him what had

127

happened and I didn't hesitate to enlarge the sentimental aspects of my dilemma. I recognised that Bob had a tender heart. He laughed when I described my efforts to get the block back on to the pistons, but sympathetically.

"I once tried to do that myself," he confessed. "And I broke a piston ring before I gave it up. It's the wrong way of doing it of course." And then he said: "Look. I'll be about ten minutes finishing this job. You'll have things to do in town. Meet me at the Albert in twenty minutes."

XIV

My DESPAIR had changed to a glorious optimism again. It was as though I'd drunk a glass of champagne. I rushed to the shops, bought milk, bread, and lest we'd have to come back to Fowey for a meal, half a dozen eggs, and a pound of rump steak. In one shop I forgot to pick up my change from a pound note and had the assistant running after me.

When I got back to the Albert Quay, one of Fowey's two restricted car parks, Bob was waiting by a small green car with its hood folded back, a pre-war Austin Seven. It looked fantastic among the chromium-plated Vauxhalls and Morrises, Sunbeams and Yankee tourers.

"I shan't mind if you laugh at it!" Bob said. "Most people do, and they can't understand my being so fond of it. I've had her six years and she's never let me down."

"But *I* can," I assured him. "That's just what I feel about *Amanda*, and I've only had her three months. How old is she?"

"1928 Model! She was over ten when the war started."

"That's the same age as my engine!"

He smiled, but said quite seriously:

"Two brothers, or two sisters, perhaps twins, and aren't twins supposed to have an affinity for each other? Are you ready to go?"

We conversed easily as we pulled across the harbour, question and answer, two human beings met by chance, getting to know each other. Bob knew I was an author. Hadn't read any of my books. Wilfred had told me he was a potter. Well he was just dabbling in it. Had built himself a kiln, had made a few things, but he had a lot to learn before he'd be able to make a living at it. So he read meters for the South West Electricity Board. I must come out and see his place, and meet Joyce. She was at Blackpool at present staying a few days with her parents. Was I going to live permanently up the creek? Was I writing another book now? I sensed a growing bond between us. We spoke each other's language.

We were not patting each other's backs but it pleased me that he liked the look of *Amanda*, at least the outside aspect of her, as we walked up the cove. She had a nice shape. He liked the way she was painted. When he looked inside however at the dismantled engine, the sludge on the thwarts, the dirty rags, the saucepans, one of whose contents I'd scattered on the bottom boards, he was silent for a while: then he said, generously:

"We've got things in a bit of a mess, haven't we? My engine wouldn't recognise its sister from this. There's only one thing to do, get the whole thing out of the boat on to something that's clear and level."

There was such a cemented space at the top of the first flight of concrete steps. It was cluttered with old ropes and other gear and I cleared it. Bob got into the boat and handed me the cylinder block which I dutifully place on to the cement. He had started unfastening the heavy bolts securing the crank case to the bearers, which I had screwed in as tightly as I could.

I asked no questions. He lifted the crank case on to the gunwale, and I held one end of it while he got out and together we carried it to the cement. He gently chided me then:

"You know, there was no need to unbolt the block from the crank case at all."

I didn't see why, but I remained guiltily silent. He had turned the crank case on to its side, and now started to remove the bolts and washers from the sump.

"Did you say you'd had the sump off?"

"Yes. And the gauze filter inside. That's where the sludge came from."

"Good," he said laconically. "You've saved me the worst job of all."

I noticed the care in which he arranged all the bolts and washers in a neat pile on the cement. He removed the sump, with its paper gasket, then the gauze filter again, carefully parking the bolts and washers. Then pliers in hand, he looked into the cavity of the crank case as a dentist might look into a patient's wide-open mouth.

"You've got it pretty clean," he said. "I doubt if it will be any worse for its dipping."

I said eagerly:

"It's possible then that she will be going again, say before to-morrow?"

With the pliers he was extracting a small split pin from the end of a bolt on one of the big ends.

He evaded my question.

"A job like this can't be hurried. We'll see how we get on. There's only one way to get the pistons back into the cylinders, and that's one at a time. I've got to disconnect the big ends and connecting rods from the crank shaft, so that the pistons are free, push them into the cylinders, put the block back, and then reconnect the big ends, and if that isn't done carefully you'll have the whole engine chewed up when you start her turning."

I was alarmed.

"Please don't think I'm trying to hurry you," I said quickly if not truthfully. "And by the way I can give you a meal when you feel like it. I've got a piece of steak. Would you like it grilled or fried?"

He was wrestling with the pin, reminding me still of a dentist with an impacted molar.

"Sorry, no steak. I'm a semi-vegetarian. Never touch red meat. A couple of boiled eggs will do for me."

"What about fish? Grilled mackerel? I've got one that was caught last night, although not by me!"

He had got the pin out.

"Ah—now you're talking. My favourite fish!"

"With new potatoes out of the garden. Peas or runner beans?"

"Runner beans every time!"

"Well, unless you need my help at present I'll start getting things ready."

"Righto. But there's no hurry. And before you go let me have all the bolts and washers you've taken out. It doesn't matter if they're mixed up, so long as they're all there."

I had an uncomfortable suspicion that some of them had rolled under the bottom boards, but I collected all I could find into one of the pans. I got my groceries from the dinghy and walked up to the house. I lifted some new potatoes from the garden, picked some tender runner beans, a spray of mint, and took these into the kitchen. I scraped the potatoes, "head" and "tailed" the beans (only culinary idiots cut young runner beans into slices), and filleted the mackerel, thinking all the time what a huge piece of luck it was meeting Bob, and how I liked him quite apart from what he was doing to the engine.

But it was only twelve o'clock, too early yet to start cooking the meal. I'd better go down and consult him about this, see how he was getting on. I walked back into the big room. I had left the door open. In front of the big window which overlooked the creek was one of the easy-chairs I had bought at the sale and had recovered. It looked, and was, extremely comfortable.

There was no hurry now. I thought I would sit down, just for a minute or two, and gloat on the view. I'd had an energetic night and morning, with no sleep for more than twenty-four hours. I sank into the chair.

And then I did a fatal thing. I closed my eyes and it was as though I had received a shot of a powerful anæsthetic. I fell asleep.

XV

I was awakened by a voice:

"Hoy. Would you like your bloody-looking steak grilled or fried?"

I rubbed my eyes: Bob was standing over me, grinning.

"I didn't want to wake you up, but I've been keeping the spuds and beans warm on the oven top, and they'll be spoiling. And very good they are too. So was that mackerel!"

"Good God! What's the time?"

"Nearly two o'clock. The boat's afloat too. When you've had a meal we'll put the engine in and get things connected up."

I had stood up, feeling a little dazed, not certain yet that this wasn't a dream.

"Don't tell me that you've finished the job!"

"All except the magneto and the timing. And by the way it was lucky I noticed the magneto in the oven. I might have roasted it. It's O.K. anyway. Quite a good spark!"

"You're a wonderful man!" I said with sincerity.

He smiled modestly. "I hope you don't mind my barging into your house like this and cooking myself a meal!"

I took it as a compliment, as a token of mutual understanding and friendship, and I told him that I was sorry I'd fallen asleep while he had been working.

"Come on," he said, "and get your dinner," adding, "I like the way you've done this place. I bet your kids are going to love it all."

I had my meal. I had another glimpse of Bob's character, as putting the kettle on he said:

"We'll wash up before we go down to the boat. Tidiness, like cleanliness is next to Godliness, even if you don't believe in God!"

We washed up. Bob wiped the table, and also swept the floor, a job I would have deferred until to-morrow, for I'd have to do it again before Marie arrived to take charge. I was afraid he might want to start on the big room too, but we safely got down to the cove.

There on the cement stood the engine, complete but for the magneto, which Bob had got in his hand. And there bravely afloat again was my darling *Amanda* no worse for her sinking. The tide was near the turn. We pulled her in until she was lightly grounded, got the engine aboard then pushed her off into deeper water. There were the routine jobs of bolting it down, connecting the exhaust, water-cooling and fuel pipes, refilling the sump with oil, the fuel tank, which had been dried out, with petrol.

These jobs I could have done myself. The timing, the meshing of the teeth of the magneto with those of the timing gear would have beaten me; and Bob himself was silent and concentrated while he carried out this, to me, complicated operation. At last he stood up and wiped his hands on still another shirt I'd provided him with.

"Well, there you are," he said. "She may start, and she may not start. Engines are very temperamental things, and in spite of this being the twin of mine, it will have a character of its own. Turn on the petrol. Is the prop in neutral?"

I had a moment of misgiving. How awful if after all, the engine wouldn't go. I turned on the petrol, saw that the propeller was in neutral. Bob half opened the throttle, flooded the carburettor, closed the choke, seized the starting handle, turned it vigorously, several times. Nothing happened. He opened the throttle wider, opened the choke, gave the handle another swing. And it did happen. With a mighty roar the

engine came to life. And I was so relieved, so pleased, so excited
I slapped Bob on the shoulder:

"You're a wizard, an absolute wizard!"

He grinned self-consciously.

"Rubbish! Cast off and let's go for a run!"

XVI

ONLY two days to go and still there was no sign of a break in the weather.

I thought I would go to bed early that night, catch up on my lost hours of sleep: get up early in the morning, tidy the whole house so as to make a good impression on Marie when she arrived to take over. A Yorkshire Scot, her standards of domestic cleanliness and order were high. The big room, which she would see first, was in a dreadful mess. I was too tired to wash up after supper. I went straight to bed, discovering when I undressed that I must have used the jacket of my best pyjamas to mop up the engine oil. It was still light, so having set my alarm for eight o'clock I tacked a thick blanket over the window and shut the door.

I was too excited to sleep. I lit a lamp and picked from the collection of books on my bedside table what during the years of my loneliness had been my greatest literary consolation, not the Bible, which was there, but Arthur Waley's translation of the Chinese classic, *Monkey*.

Monkey, made of stone, hatched from a stone egg emitted from a magic mountain, complete with every organ and limb and "nine apertures," thus capable of performing all the functions of a living being, is acclaimed King of his monkey tribe, and for several hundred years lives happily on the Mountain of Fruit and Flowers. But he is saddened by the thought that Yama, King of Death, will get him in the end. He is told that among all creatures, three kinds are not subject to Yama. They are Buddhas, Immortals and Sages.

He finds a Sage, and for twenty years is instructed in the

secrets of Immortality. He learns a spell which enables him to fly through Space (faster than any modern astronaut), which gives him the mastery of seventy-two transformations, which he demonstrates by turning himself into a pine tree and back. He calls himself Sage Equal to Heaven, illegally visits the Court of Death and erases his name from the Register, arousing the disapproval of the Celestial Authorities, and as a punishment, he is imprisoned in his mountain again for five hundred years with nothing to live on but iron pills and verdigris!

Finally he is released in order to accompany a priest called Tripitaka, and two characters called Pigsy and Sandy on a pilgrimage to India to look for certain sacred scriptures. On the way they encounter dragons and other monsters: wizards, robbers, floods, magic gales. The scriptures are found. Monkey, cleansed of his many transgressions by his devotion to Tripitaka, is elevated to the rank of an Immortal Buddha.

The mark of a good book or any other great work of art is its perpetual vitality. It goes on giving, like the heat and light of the sun. I had read *Monkey* several times from cover to cover. Every time I could find a new enchantment in it. To me it was a fairy tale (gorgeously funny and vulgar in parts but with a very profound wisdom and philosophy) that was utterly credible.

You could believe in Monkey's cloud-stepping shoes, in his ability to create a whole army of monkey soldiers simply by reciting a spell and plucking hairs from his body. His sins were many but very human, his punishments severe, but his penitence complete and his reward just and deserved. Through all the calamities that befall him his courage, his faith in himself, his sense of humour never fail. In this was the infectious inspiration of his story. Life was a dragon-beset journey for us all. I'd met and slain a few myself. Doubtless more were lurking ahead!

But I hadn't read more than a few pages of *Monkey* before my eyes began to flutter. I put the book down, blew out the lamp, and, head on the pillow, closed my eyes. Instantly I was wide awake. I lit the lamp again and had another try. The same thing happened. This time I opened another of my favourites, a volume of James Thurber whose drawings, apart from their humour, possess this same mark of inexhaustible vitality.

It was no good. My eyes closed involuntarily, I turned off the lamp and again I was awake. I got up and walked into the kitchen and surveyed my unwashed crockery, visible in the declining light of day. Should I wash up, then tackle the big room so that there would be less to do in the morning? I put the kettle on, but now I could hardly keep my eyes open. I turned off the gas, flung myself on the bed in my darkened room, shut my eyes and tried to will myself asleep, pretending I had a dentist's gas mask over my face and was inhaling nitrous oxide. I had never felt more alert, more widely awake.

To hell with it. I got up, and this time dressed, and walked through the kitchen into the big room. Should I start tidying it? It was a daylight job to do it well, and now it was practically dusk. I looked through the window. Both boats were afloat on the flowing tide. The fish should be coming in soon, and in any case there would be mackerel at the harbour mouth.

I'd go fishing, not in *Amanda*, in case anything went wrong, but in the dinghy. I had no live bait. If the fish were feeding on fry, a spinner or feather would be better than worm. And with a trolling line I would pull about until I was so tired I would just have to sleep.

I hurried down to the cove.

XVII

I HAD never in my life, so far as I knew, walked in my sleep, but I believe that somnambulists when they wake up have no memory of their nocturnal perambulations. I shall never know exactly what did happen to me that night. The evidence was that I *did* go fishing, for while there were no fish in the dinghy my trolling line was there in a hopeless tangle. I wasn't ill. I was suffering from want of sleep plus over-anxiety and excitement. I must have been in a sort of daze, pulling the boat, inexpertly fishing, half-awake, half-asleep, come back, and at last passed out completely on my bed.

I had two vividly remembered dreams. In one I was in *Amanda*, moving at full speed not on the sea, but along a road that skirted the edge of a high, steep cliff. I tried to stop her. But the more I throttled down, the faster she went, and suddenly she gave a swerve towards the cliff edge and over. I jumped out, found myself floating down on a parachute to the cliff bottom, and there on the rocks was my darling boat, not just wrecked but reduced to tiny splinters which I frantically began to sweep up with a broom and dustpan so that they wouldn't be washed away by the flowing tide.

In the other dream I heard first the harsh and persistent ringing of a bell (it must have been my alarm clock), then a knocking and a human voice. I got up (still in my dream), went to the big room door. Wilfred Denaro was standing on the veranda, with a brown paper parcel in his hand. Below him on the path was a queue of pretty teenage girls busy making bouquets from my flower beds. Wilfred handed me the parcel, which was exactly like the parcel containing the packet of tea and the socks, and the letter my wife had sent me in Wales, except that it had on it in big red letters the word EXPRESS.

Wilfred explained that the postmaster had asked him to deliver the parcel to me as no postman was available, and it seemed to be urgent. He hurried away, saying that he had to take the girls for a trip. I started opening the parcel, which contained scores and scores of sheets of brown paper tied with string, and finally came to a letter. It was from my wife and very brief. It said that she was sorry that the children couldn't come after all as she had decided to emigrate with them to Canada, and they were sailing on the *Queen Mary* in twenty-four hours!

It must have been that dream, that hideous nightmare, that awakened me. It was dark in my room, but when I pulled down the blanket I saw that the sun was shining. I looked at the time. It was nearly four o'clock, and by the sun I knew that it must be *afternoon*. Marie's train was due at five.

I hurried through the kitchen to the still untidied big room, looked through the window. Both boats were afloat at the edge of the ebbing tide, *Amanda* reassuringly completely integrated. There was just time to move her down to deep water. But I was unshaved. The room was in a mess. I glanced round it, and then I saw on the table opposite to the veranda door, a buff telegram envelope.

There *had* been a knocking at the door, a shouting, someone from the Fowey or Polruan post office trying to wake me up, who in my fantastic dream had become Wilfred.

With that dream still vividly in my mind, I picked up the telegram. But for a full minute I was too terrified to open it. It must be from my wife. Was it possible that my dream was prophetic? I tore the envelope open, unfolded the piece of paper on which the message was written in pencil. I read it. And I had to read it again, and still again before I could really convince myself that this was not a dream too.

For it was from my wife and it said:

PLANS ALTERED. ALL FIVE CHILDREN WILL ARRIVE FOWEY
STATION TODAY FIVE O'CLOCK. PLEASE MEET TRAIN.

All six of them, for it was the same train as Marie's. Could
I make it? I dashed back to my bedroom, looked at the clock.
It was five minutes past four. I dressed, put on my gum boots,
ran down to the cove. The dinghy was just grounding, but
I managed to push her off, pulled out to *Amanda*, started the
engine, took her down creek clear of the fatal buoy, dropped
anchor, pulled back and pushed the dinghy out on a trip
anchor.

I ran back to the house, shaved and washed in cold water,
gathered up my used crockery, and shoved them in a cupboard
under the sink, wiped the table top, swept the floor, and if it
wasn't up to a Yorkshire housewife's standard, cleared the
big room. And the clock of Fowey Church was striking a
quarter to five when at full speed I steered *Amanda* up-harbour
for the station quay, with the Red Ensign flying gaily, trium-
phantly, at her mast.

XVIII

MUCH can be learned about the perplexing problems of human husband and wife relationship and parenthood by an inquiry into the mating and breeding habits of the so-called lower animals. If the evolutionists are right, we share with them all a common ancestry: primordial jelly, protozoa, sea-anemones, star-fish, fish with backbones, reptiles, reptiles with wings, birds, marsupials, warm-blooded mammals, apes, tool-making and fire-using half apes, half men, with civilised man the most distinguished end-product of the many-branched evolutionary tree.

It is likely that the earliest forms of life started in the sea and reproduced their kind by splitting themselves in two. Sex, the differentiation into male and female came along later and there is a mighty long stretch of time between the mating, say, of a pair of Jurassic pterodactyls, three million years ago and that of hairy, ape-faced, mammoth-slaying Neanderthal Man and his woman (circa fifty thousand years B.C.): between this and say, a top-hat wedding in Hanover Square, with the happy couple honeymooning in the West Indies!

Yet we are all brothers or sisters under the skin. The human embryo, starting with the union of two single cells, has a fish's gill slits at one stage of its development, and we all carry a rudimentary tail at the end of our spines. Although their mothers will rarely admit it, most babies are ape-like in appearance when they are born. Their toes are prehensile, like those of all the monkey tribe. The wonder is that they can't swim like their more remote marine ancestors.

The most powerful urge among all living creatures is that

of the reproduction of their species, the mating of male and female, the care of their young. The part played by the male in this process varies. In many animals it is confined to the simple act of fertilisation. Swans mate for life, and the male jealously guards his mate and the nest during the period of incubation. He takes his share in the protection and education of the brood until they reach maturity.

But to the arrogant, lustful, barn-yard rooster a hen is a hen—black, white or speckled. He wouldn't know, and he wouldn't care, whether the eggs were hatched in a nest or incubator or sold to the Egg Marketing Board, to end up with a rasher of bacon on someone's breakfast table.

Yodelling tom-cats would not recognise their own kittens if they saw them. In our scientific age pedigree bulls do not see the cows they impregnate. The vet, with his syringe, is the proxy father. The male of a certain marine crustacean has a remoter chance of ever showing an interest or affection towards his young, for, poor devil, in the act of fertilisation the female devours him whole.

The males of some fish exhibit a perverted interest in their own progeny by eating them as they hatch from the eggs, but this may be an economical form of birth control. By contrast we have the exemplary behaviour of the lumpsucker, a fish quite common on the coasts of the British Isles.

It's a queer-looking creature with a thick body covered with big warts. Its ventral fins are modified into a sucking device with which it can attach itself firmly to rock. The female deposits her eggs in a spongy mass on to the walls of a rocky crevice among the tangles exposed and often dried out at low spring tides, and they are fertilised by the male. This done the female departs, leaving the male stuck on to the rock at the mouth of the cave to guard the eggs until they are hatched, a task which he performs with heroic fidelity and often at the cost of his life, for he will not survive a very low tide.

The female of the worm pipe fish however makes doubly sure that the duties of the male shall not end with the act of fertilisation. She glues her eggs on to his belly. But more decently she stands by him during incubation when he is virtually anchored by the weight of the eggs. At the approach of an intruder she deliberately attracts attention to herself by exaggerated jerky movements, so that he with his precious load shall be safe.

The love and devotion of the human female for her young has rightly inspired sculptors, painters and poets throughout the ages. Although the deities of all the great religions are supposed to be male, the love of common man for his children is rarely celebrated. Did Michelangelo, or Leonardo, or Raphael, or Velasquez, or Reubens ever paint a portrait of a man with a baby on his lap and no woman in sight?

The love of a father can never be so strong, so completely unselfish, as that of the mother who has given her child birth and nourishment from her breasts. But what is love after all but a strong and steady liking for another person, multiplied, expressed to perfection in a happy marriage and a brood of healthy, reasonably well-behaved kids?

Apart from the flesh and blood bond between us, I loved mine individually and collectively, with the qualification that they had at times bored me, irritated me, made me angry, but never to a point where I had been tempted to inflict physical punishment apart from a gentle token slap. And no father, long parted from his loved ones, no soldier, sailor, Arctic explorer, or time-served convict could have awaited with greater eagerness a reunion with his loved ones than I did for the arrival of the train at Fowey that summer afternoon: for the clatter of the home signal falling, the distant whistle of the engine, and at last the sight of the train itself as it came round a bend in the track towards the station.

It drew into the platform, stopped. Because of the holiday rush there were extra coaches on it, all packed. Fearful that after all something might have happened to stop them coming, I dashed along the platform from the guard's van end, peering through the windows. Dodging among the passengers who were getting out, I reached the engine end. They were not there. All the compartments were now empty. I swung round, and then stopped, momentarily petrified. I saw a group of four children standing near to the distant guard's van end, and with them a slender adult female in a summer dress, holding a little boy by the hand, her back towards me.

The four were my own. I would have recognised them a mile off. The little boy could only be my last born. *Was it his mother who was holding his hand?* It was her height, her figure. Had the yearned for miracle happened at last? She turned, so that I could see her face. It was not my wife, but Marie, and it *was* a good thing that one's thoughts are private, for I would not have liked dear Marie to have known what passed through my mind when I recognised her; that as I had watched the train coming into the platform, I had completely forgotten that she was arriving by it too. She must have met the children unexpectedly when they had all changed into the local train.

I swallowed the lump that had come into my throat. The children had spotted me, were waving their hands, racing up the platform, Marie discreetly waiting. And I ran towards them, to catch the winner of the race in my arms; to hear again that lovely word, "Daddy!", "Daddy!", "Daddy!".

XIX

ANY MAN with a normal affection for his children would have found it easy to be the perfect, generous, tolerant, good-tempered, amusing, loving father on a holiday like this. Pen just a couple of young children in a nursery on a rainy day, supply them with picture books, paint boxes, games, toys galore and it won't be long before you have them squabbling with each other, smashing things up, anything to direct the attention of their parent or parents to their discontent. What they need of course is space, the open air, somewhere where they can run about, climb trees, make mud pies, splash about in water, all manifestly impossible in winter, but here and now to be had in full measure.

Had I been a millionaire, I could not have planned and provided things more successfully. They were thrilled with the house itself, the ex-ship's bunks and mattresses (another "war disposal" bargain) I had fitted in their bedrooms: with the size of the big room, where they could dance to the music of radio or gramophone. The bathroom with its disciplinarian implications did not interest them so much, but they watched the pumping of the water with the ex-ship's fire engine with great glee.

But it was the cove and the creek and the boats that excited and delighted them most. From half tide (flood or ebb) to high, there was safe water and a hard shingle bottom for them to bathe, swim or paddle. *Amanda* was moored well out in the creek, but except at low tide, the dinghy was available, and I had also acquired for them another war disposal bargain, an R.A.F. inflatable rubber dinghy, complete with hand paddles, telescopic mast and a little red sail. Here, however, I exercised a parental precaution. These ingenious craft which had saved many a ditched airman's life during the war were potentially dangerous for children. With an off-shore wind or current they could move swiftly out to deep water, and although there was no such wind or current in the cove or creek, I tethered it with a stout line. Old Pa lumpsucker guarding his eggs could not have been more zealous!

Ann, our first-born (I'd called her Amelia in *Love in the Sun* and she was now seventeen), Henrietta fifteen, Simon twelve, Patrick ten, were all good swimmers, but they were never swimming out of their depth unless I was in unostentatious attendance, either swimming myself, or in the dinghy. Even so I felt happier when they were all in the cove, splashing each other, ducking under water and retrieving pebbles, pushing each other off the rubber dinghy.

It was good to see them all so happy in the sunshine, to hear their shrieks of laughter: to have Shawn clasping my hand, pulling me over the shingle to show me a tiny crab he had found at the water's edge. When I had made my first encounter with him at the station, I'd been careful not to rush things; he had stared at me, unsmiling, as a child does meeting a stranger, weighing him up, and then still unsmiling, he had made the rather astonishing remark:

"You've had your hair cut!" which happened to be true. But his hand was in mine when we had entered the big room: and again he had stared, and then to my own huge delight said with a real chuckle:

"I like this!"

I could say with a justifiable pride, yet not of course with complete detachment, that he was a lovely boy. He was dark, like his mother, with a lean brown body, eyes sparkling with vitality. In this respect he was like Patrick, but Simon was fair, more heavily built. Henrietta too was fair, and temperamentally very like Simon, easy going, jolly. Ann, whose hair had been flaxen as a small child, had developed into a brunette, yet of them all she was the one most physically like her mother. She was, and that may have been because of her age, inclined to moodiness. Indeed I sensed an incipient artistic temperament. She would let herself go when she was playing with the others, but she had made a bee-line for my bookshelves on arrival, and frequently she would detach herself from the gang and settle herself down in some secluded spot to read; but never, I observed rather sadly, choosing one of my own titles. It would be *Mansfield Park* or *The Brothers Karamazov* or the plays of Bernard Shaw or Chekhov. Once I saw her apparently engrossed in *War and Peace* but it was back on its shelf next day.

Although by the Christian faith, and by my own divergent faith of Christian Humanism, it was morally wrong for the parents of such a family to be living apart, and especially wrong for the children themselves, I could not honestly feel that any of them seemed the worse for it. There was no doubt that they were being as well looked after in their mother's home, or in the various schools they were attending, as they had ever been before we had parted. They were all well nourished, physically fit, well mannered.

Were husbands and fathers really necessary once a family was in existence? Many a family had been permanently deprived of a father by the war. The shock and grief of death became softened in time. Many a child was born posthumously. Were they any the worse for never knowing a father? It was a gloomy, disconcerting thought, which under the present circumstances I could not entertain. Here I was with my children, and we were all happy.

Marie was a darling. She was fond of my wife. She had made it clear from the start that she would preserve a strict neutrality. It was a pity that we had parted. She would like to see us make up our differences, and it didn't matter who was to blame. The children came first. She couldn't take their mother's place, and she wasn't going to try. She was here to do a woman's job in helping them to enjoy their holiday, cooking their meals, keeping them and the place reasonably clean and tidy. She didn't want me messing about in the kitchen. I could bring in the potatoes and vegetables from the garden. Ann and Henrietta would help with the washing up, making the beds. She would join us on the beach, or in the boats when she had done her jobs. But the more time I spent outside with the children the better.

At half tide on the ebb (and the tides were now full spring) the shingle gave way to the mud of the creek and bathing was not practicable as the water in the creek was then too shallow. There was, however, between shingle and soft mud, a belt of mixed mud and shingle where the ragworms used for bait were found by digging with a fork. And on the harbour side of the cove where the cliff projected into the creek, there was a narrow winding channel in the mud, extending down creek to the permanent deep water of the harbour. I had marked the course of it by sticking bamboos at intervals into its banks. Scoured by the water of the ebbing tide, its bottom was hard, and there were scores of flattish stones, giving surface anchorage to tufts of bladder wrack, and on their underside, shelter to a variety of marine animals.

Raising these stones on edge was indeed like raising the lid of a treasure chest. The children, in their bathing garments but with their feet protected with plimsolls were wild with excitement. I had been unable to provide them with an aquarium, but they had found a galvanised bath under the house, carried it down to the foot of the cove steps and half filled it with sea water. They had buckets and jam jars, with string handles for collecting.

I took no active part in this treasure hunt. The stones were not big enough to need my help. But I was the referee, and I insisted that every stone should be put back in its original position, for if it was turned completely over the surface weed would rot, spoiling the underpart as a shelter. I was on call of course.

"Daddy, Daddy. There's an eel, come quick!"

"Ann, do help me with this stone. It's so heavy."

"I've got a star-fish!"

"Look what I've got. A little green fish. Patrick, where's your jar?"

"O-oh, look! There's a wizard anemone! Daddy, how can I get it off?"

I did offer to help Shawn with a stone which I judged to be too heavy for him, but he said indignantly:

"I'll do, I'll do," and he did do it unassisted and yelled with delight when he saw under it a lovely red star-fish.

All these living treasures would be taken to the bath, and by low tide it would be swarming with eels, gobies, tiny green wrasse, shore crabs; a scandalous overcrowding which called for an unpopular parental edict that when the tide came up again they should be given their freedom and returned to the sea.

But before that happened there would be a greater excitement. At dead low water the winding channel in the mud would be almost dry, and remain so during the period called the slack. By then we would have the prawn nets and empty buckets ready. The tide at last would turn. The mud banks down the creek would still be bare, but you would see the water advancing up the channel in a miniature tidal bore. As the crest of it drew near, the surface of the water behind it (turgid with mud) would be seething with a concentrated shoal of prawns, some of them leaping into the air. All we had to do was dip the nets in with a scooping movement and out again, empty the catch into the buckets and go on until the water was welling over the banks of the channel, when the shoal would break up and spread over the whole creek.

Boiled in sea water, with added salt, until they were brick red, these prawns were delicious, and the children gorged on them. But exciting though the catching of them was, this was not real fishing. Wait till we got among the mackerel in *Amanda*!

XX

The weather remained fine, with only a gentle off-shore breeze to ruffle the level surface of the sea, yet before setting out on our first fishing trip I spent an hour on board *Amanda*, checking everything as carefully as if I were bound for a voyage across the Atlantic. She still leaked a little. This probably was because of the sun and the dry air preventing some of her seams from closing. I took the bilge pump to bits, greased the moving parts and saw that the suction pipe was clear of obstructions.

I checked all the vital tools, the compass, anchors, the stays of the mast, and various ropes. I saw that the oil in the sump was at its right level, took out all the plugs and cleaned their points with a wire brush, filled the petrol tank, oiled the moving parts of the reversing gear, renewed the grease in the inboard propeller shaft gland. There were four ex-M.N. life-jackets in the cabin, and I had bought a child's kapok life-jacket for Shawn, as the only non-swimmer, which despite his protests, I insisted he should wear whenever we were water-borne. Pa Lumpsucker, indeed!

It was to be an afternoon excursion only. We'd be back for tea and bathing in the cove at high tide. Marie wouldn't come. She had letters to write, and she'd be quite happy sunbathing down by the cove, perhaps pulling up the creek in the dinghy. She came with us in the dinghy out to *Amanda*, and stood by until we had cast off and I had got the engine going. It had started on the first kick, and away we went down creek at medium speed, for the harbour, now absolutely packed with yachts, cabin cruisers and smaller pleasure craft.

All the children except Ann, who was perched up on the deck with a book on her lap, wanted to steer, but I was adamant in my refusal with the harbour so crowded. As well as private craft there were now scores of "drive yourself" motor boats for hire, their "drivers" understandably ignorant of the Standard Regulations For Preventing Collision at Sea. One such boat with a very towny-looking couple and two cocky schoolboys on board, one of the boys about Patrick's age at the tiller, was overtaking us on the wrong side, port instead of starboard, and Simon cried:

"Daddy, can't we go faster? Don't let them beat us. Shall I open the throttle?"

Again I was adamant in my refusal. The boat did overtake us, and breaking another rule cut across our bows so that I had to throttle down and take quick avoiding action, and to the greater annoyance of my own crew the boy at the tiller actually laughed and waved his hand at us derisively.

"What an absolute twerp," Simon cried.

Patrick shook his fist.

"I'd like to slosh him one on the jaw!"

"Shut up, both of you," admonished Henrietta. "You're not setting a nice example to Shawn talking like that," adding, as though she feared she was usurping my authority, "are they, Daddy?"

I liked the way that Henrietta, two years younger than dreamy, temperamental Ann, seemed to regard herself as responsible for her brothers. She didn't bully them or what would have been worse, nag them, but she kept them up to scratch with their table manners and general behaviour, and on the whole they took it well.

"You're quite right, Henrietta," I said: then feeling rather hypocritically like a parson giving a religious talk in Children's Hour on the B.B.C., I added: "The best way to take an insult is to ignore it. Whosoever shall smite thee on the right cheek, turn to him the other also."

"Gosh!" Patrick cried indignantly, "I wouldn't do that. No fear."

"Well, you should," said Henrietta, "because it says so in the Bible."

Preachers should practise what they preach, but I had an irresistible impulse to do otherwise. The offending boat, now about three lengths ahead, was steering for the harbour mouth. There was plenty of room on either side of her. I opened the throttle to full. The engine roared. *Amanda* forged ahead.

"We're going to lick them. Hooray!" Simon shouted.

"Hooray! Hooray!" Patrick echoed. "That'll teach them to swank. Come on, Daddy, come on!"

I saw that even Henrietta had a Rolls-Royce smile on her face as we drew level with the boat on the correct starboard side, passed her, making her rock with our wake. That Ann was smiling too. They all waved to the boat's occupants, who however looked the other way—cowardly admission of defeat which made me feel rather sorry for them. But by then we were passing out of the harbour mouth. I throttled down, and with some trepidation, took off the lid of the engine box. I was relieved to see that my ancient Austin Seven, although very hot, seemed no worse for her violent exertion.

It was a gorgeous day. The off-shore wind was still very gentle. The sea was level, a deep Mediterranean blue with moving patches of purple made by the shadows of the slowly drifting puffs of fine weather clouds. In the lee of the cliffs was a belt of dead windless calm. Here and spread out seawards were scores of small pleasure craft, some with inboard or out-board motors, some only with oars, moving in circles, trolling for mackerel.

Personally I was rather contemptuous of this sort of fishing. Of all sea fish mackerel are the silliest. It requires no art to catch them. When they are on the feed (and provided that you can find the shoals they always are) they will snatch at any sort of bait that bears the vaguest resemblance to herring or pilchard fry, their favourite food: a glittering metal spinner, a piece of rubber tube, a bit of white rag, a hen's feather, even a bare polished hook.

True that they are among the most beautiful of all British fish in shape and colour with their rakish streamlined bodies, dark green-black mottled backs and iridescent silver bellies: that they fight hard when hooked, that when fresh they are extremely good to eat. But when you have seen one you have seen all. They are as identical as daisies in a field. In a shoal all of them are the same size, and while occasionally you do get an extra big one it would be a very big one indeed if it weighed two pounds.

The children however were not going to share my choosiness.

"When do we start, Daddy?"

We had turned east, close under the tall Polruan cliff. I had to explain that when trolling in a boat of *Amanda's* size only two lines could be used at the same time.

"Everyone must take turns. As soon as one of you catches a fish, he'll hand his line over. That's only fair. Who's going to catch the first two?"

"Me—me!" cried Shawn. "I want to catch a fish!"

"So do I!" cried Patrick.

"I suppose as the eldest son, I ought to stand down!" Simon said philosophically. "Although really it ought to be ladies first!"

"How polite we are getting," Henrietta mocked, but not unkindly. "I don't want to be first. But what about Ann?"

Ann, her book with a marker in it was sprawled on the foredeck, her head near the stem, and gazing overboard.

"Thanks a lot, but I'm quite happy where I am. I've just seen an absolutely heavenly jelly fish!"

I tactfully solved the problem of precedence by asking Simon to take the wheel. There was deep water close up to the cliff foot and there were no other boats within dangerous distance. He sprang to it eagerly. I took out the two trolling lines from the tackle box. The bait was the conventional spinner with a three fathom cast of nylon strong enough to hold a ten pound fish, a lead "sinker" furnished with swivels, and a moderate length of stout cotton line. I paid the first one out, made it fast to a cleat and gave it to Shawn to hold.

Before I had time to pay out Patrick's line, Shawn gave an excited shout:

"I've got one—I've got one!"

He started hauling in.

There had been such a glut of mackerel for the last week or so that I knew that it was possible that he had hooked a fish straight away, but when I put my hand on the line I had to tell him it wasn't so. It was just the weight of the sinker and the pull of the boat, and I gave the line an imitation wiggle, to show him what a fish *did* feel like.

"You'll soon get one," I said confidently. I paid out the other line, handed it over to Patrick.

The Polruan cliff was much higher and steeper than the cliffs to the west of Fowey, and its top was almost level for half a mile eastwards. Then it lowered and there was a wide shingly indentation called Lantic Bay, bounded to the east by rocky Pencarrow Head. The bay was a favourite fishing ground and when we opened it at last (still with no fish) several boats were moving about it. But I could not see any of their occupants hauling in, as some of them would have been if they had struck a mackerel shoal. Beyond Pencarrow Head were several smaller coves, and then the cliffs rose again precipitously to drop again to the cove and famous fishing port of Polperro, five miles away, but to us invisible.

With Simon steering to my signals we made several circuits of the bay without success. By then all the other boats had moved off. I was worried. What had happened to the fish? Conditions of tide and weather and time of day were all ideal. Never had I felt so anxious to see a fish caught. Children are so easily bored. You've got to be an adult and a confirmed angling addict to appreciate that half the joy of the sport is in the anticipatory and often long protracted waiting.

Shawn was the first to express his disillusionment.

"Why can't I catch anything, Daddy? You said I'd get one soon."

Then Patrick said:

"Shall I steer now, Simon, so that you can fish? I don't mind your taking my turn."

"I'd rather steer," Simon answered firmly. "Let Henrietta have a go."

"*I* want to steer!" said Shawn.

"You're too young," said Simon.

"Well, I don't want to fish, 'coz there aren't any."

I began to feel like a comedian whose jokes were falling flat on his audience. I put my arms around Shawn, who was on the point of tears and said, but without conviction:

"You'll catch one soon, don't you worry!"

"Come up here with me, Shawn, and look for the jelly fish," put in Ann.

Shawn surrendered his line to Henrietta. We were now close to Pencarrow Head. Some of the boats had gone round it to the next cove, but although the engine was running well, I was taking no risks. We were already far enough away from home.

"Turn her round and steer a bit out to sea," I said to Simon. "Perhaps we've been fishing too near the shore. We'll find the mackerel soon. Out a bit and then back towards the harbour."

The clearest indication that a shoal had been located would have been a concentration of boats: but although there were scores of them in sight they were still scattered. Among them, about half a mile distant, I suddenly recognised the green pulling pram of my old friend Sharkie Tomlin, himself at the oars. He would know where the fish were, if indeed there were any. I pointed:

"Steer for that green dinghy, Simon!"

We had halved the distance to Sharkie when an exciting thing happened. Just ahead of us a huge black dolphin, it was as big as *Amanda*, broke the surface of the water—up—over—curving like a wave—and down again, emitting a loud snort from its blow hole. Then came another, even closer on our starboard side, with three more following.

Anticipating the children's alarm I shouted:

"It's all right. They're only dolphins. Quite harmless."

I needn't have worried. The dolphins were going ahead at a great pace on a course almost direct for the green dinghy, their triangular dorsal fins cutting the water like a knife. But they swerved before they reached it, and passed no nearer than they had passed us, and I saw Sharkie, who was in his shirt sleeves, ship his oars, stand up and shake his fists at them. He had seen us too. I told Henrietta and Patrick to haul in their lines. I stopped the engine and taking the tiller, steered in close to him. He too had hauled in his line.

"How are you doing, Sharkie?" I called. "Any fish?"

He raised his hands in disgust.

"Not a one, and I've been pullin' about more than two hours! See them blow fish? That's what's done it, the varmints. They've frightened all the mackerel away. Yesterday out here I could 'ave filled the boat by this time. You got any?"

"Not a bite!"

"Thought as much. There's no one caught a fish that I've seen. It's no good when them varmints is about. I'm packing up. I've had enough. Nice to see you with your family again. You've got a real handsome crew."

"They're feeling a bit fed up about the fishing, Sharkie. Do you think there's a chance of getting any other sort of fish anywhere, or will the dolphins have scared everything?"

" 'Ave you got any worms?"

I had taken the precaution of digging some ragworms that morning, and they were in the cabin.

"Yes. Plenty of worms, and I've got hand-lines."

"Then you go into Coombe and drop anchor. You'll maybe get a wrasse or two, oniy they'm no good to eat. Don't let your lines go deeper than three fathoms or you'll lose your hooks on the weed."

Wrasse are rock fish; thick set, sluggish, rather like the

157

lumpsucker, without its warts. There are several varieties and some of them beautifully marked with coloured mottlings and stripes. They are very bony however and are despised by anglers.

But any fish would be better than none! It didn't take long to reach Coombe, to westwards of the harbour mouth. I dropped anchor within a hundred yards of the beach. There was no problem of precedence now. I had hand lines for all, each with a lead sinker and a single hook. Simon passed me the tin of worms. I baited the first line.

"Come on, Shawn," I said. "See if you can catch the first!"

He was still up on the deck with Ann, who had just opened her book again.

"I don't want to, 'coz there just aren't any," he said disconsolately.

I handed the line to Patrick.

"All right, you take the first line. Don't let the sinker go down too far."

I reached for another line, but this time it was Patrick who gave an excited shout:

"I've got one! Gosh! It *is* pulling!"

He was hauling in. I looked overboard, saw it coming up, a fish that I didn't at first recognise. He hauled the last three feet of line. The fish broke water. He swung it inboard, and he shouted exultantly:

"*Got* it. Hooray!" and there was a chorus of hoorays. Shawn jumped down from the deck, shouting, "It's my turn now. I want to catch a fish." Ann, her book closed, followed as eagerly.

But Henrietta had taken the second line from me, baited the hook herself, and while I was taking Patrick's fish off the hook she said, quietly and confidently:

"Here's another."

She swung it into the boat. Both fish were sea bream. They had reddish backs, silver bellies, measuring about nine inches from head to tail. Their dorsal fins were furnished with sharp spines, and they had to be held very carefully while removing the hook. I remembered that they were particularly good to eat, with a firm white flesh like that of the gurnard. Henrietta rebaited the hook and generously handed over her line to Shawn. I'd already baited Patrick's. Both Simon and now Ann were waiting for their lines, but before I could help them, Patrick and Shawn were shouting excitedly, "I've got one, I've got one!"

It was clear that we had struck a shoal of voracious fish.

"You'll have to do your own baiting," I shouted to Simon and Ann, as I unhooked Shawn's fish and then Patrick's.

"I'll help," said the ever generous Henrietta.

"I can bait my own," Simon said, adding a little ironically, "but I'll bait yours first, Ann, if you don't like the job."

"Thanks," Ann said, "I can do it myself, but I never did like worms, they're too wriggly."

This was indeed more than I had bargained for. No sooner had they got their lines over than both of them were hauling in, and with Patrick and Shawn doing the same, I was faced with four fish. I was thankful at least that when I had rigged up these lines I had furnished them with only a single hook, otherwise I might have had eight flapping fish to deal with at the same time.

Not that I would have minded. I had no desire to fish myself. I was perfectly content doing what I could to keep the ball rolling. It was a joy to listen to the excited shouts of the children, to know that they were completely happy on this perfect summer afternoon on the shining sea. As such I would remember this, and I believed that they would remember it too, like Wordsworth and his daffodils, "fluttering and dancing in the breeze."

My only worry was that the bait was getting low. There was going to be a fuss when the last worm had gone and we had to pack up for home.

XXI

IT WAS easy for me to act the loving father. There was no opportunity for any of the children to be bored, the thing most likely to test the patience and temper of a parent. Apart from the joys of the cove and the creek, the bathing, the stone turning, the prawns and the boats, and these never palled, there was always something interesting for them to do. Ann had her books, but she had a passion for flowers, and without even a hint from me, weeded and watered all the flower beds. Henrietta, whose interest in gardening was strong but more practical, did the same with the vegetables and fruit bushes.

I gave the boys the run of my workshop. They made little boats, and tried them out in the stream or the cove. They dammed the stream, making pools and waterfalls. With some of the rough boards left over from the roof of the hut they built a Peter Pan house of sorts in the oak tree on which I had fixed their swing. They made fires on the beach with dead branches, and boiled winkles.

We had to make our daily trips to Polruan or Fowey for shopping, and to collect our mail, in *Amanda* if the tide was right and everyone wanted to go, otherwise in the dinghy. I was far from rolling in money, but I never refused them an ice-cream or a lolly when we were in town, or even peaches at tenpence apiece. Perhaps I would have been a better father if I had given them a lecture on the virtue of thrift and self-denial. I might have told them that when I was a little boy my weekly pocket money was a halfpenny, that an ice-cream, available only at our annual Whitsuntide Fair, was something that had to be carefully measured against a ride on the roundabouts or the swings or a go at the coconuts. But I refrained from moralising. We were all on holiday. When the first Sunday came, I dutifully asked them if any of them wished to go to church or chapel or Sunday school. There were no volunteers; I did not ask them again.

Yet my own behaviour was exemplary. I never showed any anger when three of my ten-inch Beethoven gramophone records were smashed. I didn't swear when I found Patrick using my best chisel as a screwdriver. Marie herself remarked on my restraint:

"I think you're wonderful, Leo, the way you seem to have stopped swearing. You used to swear like a trooper. You're quite a reformed character. You even said 'blow' the other day instead of your usual ' Christ '! It's nice but it isn't natural!"

"I'm trying hard to be at least a temporary saint," I said. "The word 'blow' certainly comes unnaturally to my tongue."

Alas for precept and restraint. I was walking down to the cove and overheard Simon and Patrick having a mild argument about something.

"Where is the bloody thing? You had it last, Patrick."

"No, I damn' well didn't. You bloody well had it yourself. Look, it's there, right in front of your nose."

"Well, I'm damned! So it is. A thousand pardons, old boy!"

Like Brer Rabbit, I "said nuthin' an' lay low."

Yes, it was easy. In winter-time, and in the inclement months of autumn and spring, the healthiest of children catch colds, mumps, chicken-pox, measles. In a large family there is no end to worries and anxieties, the onus falling inevitably on the mother. Here in the fresh ozone-charged air and sunshine, with plenty of good food rich in natural vitamins there were no ailments, not a cough or a sneeze or a headache.

We usually had company for tea when the tides were suitable: never the vicar, so the best china was not called for. We entertained our guests on a lawn I had made between the house and the stream, a sort of help-yourself service with the tea in mugs. Wilfred was a frequent caller, always with a boat-load of children. But our most popular visitors were Bob Shoe-bridge and his wife Joyce. Bob was having a fortnight's holiday from his detested meter reading. They'd arrive in Bob's little sailing dinghy, its hull red with a snow-white sail, and all the children would rush down to welcome them.

Despite their financial worries, that Bob was unable to devote all his time and energy to his chosen profession of pottery, that he was indeed a frustrated artist, they were a happy couple. They were well matched: Bob with his actor's loose, lean jaws, sensitive mobile lips and deep masculine voice: Joyce more reserved, almost diffident, and with the serene beauty of a young madonna. She had a lovely face.

They'd been married several years and were childless, but both of them were fond of children, and possessed Marie's gift for winning their confidence and affection. They'd had an unsettled life, doing all sorts of jobs, living in lodgings, or furnished cottages, or flats, caravans, even camping, but always on the lookout, in their Austin Seven, for a place of their own in the country, where they could live permanently and Bob could build his pottery kiln. This they had at last found, a tumble-down building on the wooded edge of a worked out and flooded china clay pit half-way to St. Austell, which Bob, a disciple of Thoreau, had called Waldon's Pond.

I hadn't seen this place of theirs yet. I hadn't seen any of Bob's pottery. He was extremely modest about it. But I agreed with Wilfred that Bob was a natural character actor and comedian. He had the face, the voice, the spontaneous creative wit. He never tried to be funny, or to impress. He didn't make wise-cracks or tell conventional funny stories. All his "acts" were spontaneous. Bathing with the children in the cove, he suddenly took an armful of seaweed, draped it over his head and shoulders, and with fronds of it hanging from his mouth to make a moustache and beard, and prawn net for a trident, gave a brilliant caricature of Father Neptune. The children were hysterical. He would sing snatches of opera, guying, in tremulous falsetto, a portly Madame Butterfly, pushing a cushion into his shirt to make a bosom, gesturing like a prima donna.

In addition to this he had an extraordinary gift for narrative. He was a born story-teller, with a strong sense of the comic. There was a comic side even to his experiences as a meter reader; a job which took him in all weathers over a wide area, country as well as town. There were meters to be read at the homes of the rich, where he'd have to knock or ring the bell at the tradesmen's entrance and be regarded with contemptuous tolerance by a haughty butler or a cook. There were remote farms and cottages where he'd be as welcome as a prodigal son, and regaled with tea and cake.

His visit to one lonely farm was at a time when a convict described as dangerous was on the run from Dartmoor prison. Bob knocked at the door, got no answer. Then an elderly woman, her face as white as a sheet, appeared at a bedroom window, a double-barrel shot-gun in her hand.

"What do 'e want?" she shouted.

She was pointing the gun in Bob's direction. Bob's mouth was so dry he could hardly speak.

"I've come to read the meter."

"How do I know you'm from the electricity, that you'm not a murderer?"

Bob took out his official identity card and held it up, his hand shaking. She was not convinced.

"How do I know that ain't a forgery? Don't 'e try breaking in. You be off now, quick."

It was the sudden arrival of the farmer himself from the fields that saved the situation.

I listened to Bob's recital of such incidents as these with professional envy, but also with a feeling of exasperation. It was not just the verbal telling of them that impressed me, but the brilliant way in which he mimed each one of his characters, the haughty butler, the friendly cottagers, the farmer's wife. Why should a man with such a gift have to be reading meters for a living, when thousands of men of lesser talent were earning colossal salaries or fees on stage, or in films or radio.

But when I suggested to him that he might try to get an audition with the B.B.C. and give just the story of the farmer's wife as a sample, he laughed.

"I'd be scared stiff. I just couldn't do it."

I couldn't resist taking advantage of Bob's histrionic gifts by playing a little trick on the children. He shared my antipathy to clergymen. The children were down in the cove. I had among my possessions a black Stetson hat, and with a dinner jacket, a white cardboard dog collar, and dark sun glasses, and a little mascara provided by the ladies, Bob made a tolerable impersonation of a vicar.

"Ask them," I said, "why the hell they haven't been to service or Sunday school."

I walked down the path with him, trying to look as serious as the occasion demanded. The children were all in the water, shouting and laughing as usual. As we reached the steps, however, and they saw us, they were suddenly silent, all staring at us, in surprise.

"The vicar has come to see you," I said.

"Indeed, yes," the vicar said sternly. "Yes, indeed. Listen to me. On six days shalt thou labour, on the seventh day thou shalt do no manner of work or (either Bob had forgotten the rest or he was merely improvising) play. How is it that none of you came to church or Sunday school last Sunday. I trust that next Sunday——"

One of the children screamed:

"It's Bob—it's Bob!"

And there were shrieks of laughter as the children rushed to mob him. The game was up.

They loved Bob. They were not likely to forget him and his comic acts when, their holiday over—I was dreading that day—

they went back home. They would tell their mother about him, and many other pleasant and exciting things that had happened, and were still to happen. Each of them would be a subtle unconscious propagandist on my behalf, supporting, I dared to hope, a final reconciliation. I was still an optimist.

XXII

But I was not optimistic enough to believe that the weather would last the whole of the holiday, half of which had already gone without a drop of rain or any variation in the succession of fine warm days. The wind, what there was of it, held steadily off the land so that the sea was smooth, and, in the lee of the cliffs, with scarcely a ripple, so that one could land in any of the coastal coves in perfect safety.

It was inevitable that the break would come, and I never relaxed my precautions. Before setting off on any of our trips, I would listen to the radio weather forecast, scan the sky, note from the drift of the clouds, if any were visible, the direction of the wind: and no matter how exciting our activities when we were ashore on the coast, I'd always have my weather eye open.

We'd not listen to Marie's excuses that she had letters to write or wanted to get on with the housework, or that *Amanda* would be overcrowded, on these occasions. We'd tow the dinghy with us, and two of the children could troll from her while we were under way. The big shoals of mackerel had not returned inshore since the coming of the dolphins, but pollack, and bass too, will go for a spinner. After that afternoon among the bream however, none of the children had acquired the essential patience for this sort of fishing, which on most of our trips had been completely unsuccessful. But it suited Ann to sit in the dinghy, with nothing to distract her from her book.

We were on our way to Lantic Bay, on the same course we had taken on our first trip, with Ann alone in the dinghy. She had put the trolling line over, and she was at least making a pretence of fishing, holding the line with one hand, her precious book in the other.

Suddenly she shrieked, put the book down—for once not marking the page—stood up, both hands on the line:

"*I've got one.* It's huge. I can hardly hold it. O-o-oh, it's a monster!"

"I'll give you a help!" Simon shouted gallantly. "Don't let it go!"

"No. I don't want any help," Ann shouted back, and now hauling in. "But it *is* huge. It's terrific."

I stopped the engine, pulled the dingy in until it was nearly alongside, and landing net in hand got in.

I could tell by the way the line was cutting the water that Ann was not exaggerating. It was a big one, either a pollack or bass, bigger than anything I had caught since my return to Cornwall. But I wasn't going to take it from her, glad that she didn't ask me to.

"Don't be in a hurry," I cautioned. "Let the line go if it pulls very hard. Haul in if it starts to slack off. Don't hurry!"

"Perhaps it's a dolphin," one of the children shouted.

"It feels more like a whale," gasped Ann, "but it's coming, it's coming."

I was peering over the side, watching the line, thinking now of Sharkie's famous pollack, and praying as even Christian Humanists can pray that this one wouldn't get off. Ann was still hauling. Suddenly I saw it, a gleam of silver, about three fathoms down, swimming from side to side. It was a bass I thought and a beauty.

"Steady now," I cautioned, "pay out, if it makes a sudden rush. But don't try to lift it in. When it's near enough I'll grab it with the net."

It did make a last frantic effort to escape. Ann let the line slip through her hands, then, and old Sharkie could not have done it better, checked it, held on, and started to haul again. I still thought the fish was a bass. No pollack could have gleamed like that. It came nearer, still zig-zagging, still fighting. I'd got the net in the water. It gave a rush that took it under the dinghy out of sight. For one moment I thought it had gone. But the line was taut.

"Stop hauling," I yelled. "Just hold on."

Ann held on: and the fish came back, straight into the net. I heaved it up, over the gunwale, on to the bottom of the dinghy, and although it was still in the net I saw what it was. The word "Christ" involuntarily escaped my lips, the ultimate expression of my amazement and delight. For it was a salmon trout, weighing, we were to prove later, eight and a half pounds. Only once in my life had I seen one caught with a bait in the open sea, and it was no bigger than a mackerel, with its fins and tail half eaten away with lice. This was in prime condition. I killed it and Ann proudly held it up for everyone to see. From then on, there was no lack of volunteers for trolling in the dinghy. Ann, the champion, was content to sprawl on the fore deck with her book, or looking for jelly fish.

XXIII

EACH OF the coves we visited had its own special interest and charm. The beach at Lantic Bay was composed entirely of shingle, not the shingle of our own protected cove where the stones were mostly shaley and flat, but of rounded pebbles ground smooth as marbles by the mountainous waves that crashed into the bay in stormy weather. The cliffs immediately above the beach were high and steep, but they were lower and more broken and rugged where they curved seawards to Pencarrow Head.

There was always plenty of driftwood at high water mark and other treasures to be found among the debris thrown up by the storms; for this was beyond the range of local beach-combers. There were fishermen's buoys and corks, glass balls that came from trawlers, wood sabots—alas only single ones, never pairs—that must have come from the Breton "crabbers" who to the annoyance of the Cornish inshore fishermen frequently poached their crab and lobster grounds.

Lantic, with the sea smooth was ideal for bathing. The water was never quite so warm as it was in the creek. It was slightly saltier however, more buoyant, more invigorating. If it chilled you could stretch yourself on the sun-baked shingle and soon be ready to go in again. There was a spring at the cliff foot for our kettle. The children loved making fires to boil the water for tea.

Yet Lantic was less good for other activities. The rocks that bounded the beach were too exposed to support weed or animal life, even barnacles or limpets. There were no loose stones to turn over. To find these we'd have to go round

Pencarrow Head—and I never did this without a little trepidation—to Lantivet Bay. Here, protected by the headland from
the prevalent south-westerly gales of winter were a series of
little coves, some with shingle beaches, some just narrow and
irregular chasms leading into the cliff foot from the deep water.

It was not a place for bathing. The rocks at low tide were
thickly grown with kelp and cord weed. Exploring among
them then (and the tides were spring again) was like exploring
the sea bed itself. There were cracks, little caves in the rocks,
adorned with anemones. There were sea urchins galore, and
star-fish crimson and purple, much bigger than the ones we
found in the creek. There were clear pools among the rocks,
swarming with tiny gobies, and other rock fish. And, although
these took more finding, there were real eating crabs, the
common smooth one and the prickly spiny spider-crab, and
Simon was able to score off Ann and her salmon trout by
finding, although he left me to pull it out of a crevice, a fair-sized
lobster.

Ann's book would be left among our picnic things whenever
we were ashore at Lantivet. Simon and Patrick were the
primitive practical crab hunters looking for things that could be
eaten. Ann was more interested in the æsthetic; the anemones,
the exquisitely shaped and coloured sea slugs she found under
the stones, the small tinted sea weeds that grew among the
roots of the kelp. Henrietta, in whom the instincts of the
hunter and the artist were combined, was content to be with
Shawn, helping him climb the most difficult of the rocks,
turning over the stones.

Between two of the coves there was a massive rock standing
out from the cliff foot so that at high tide it would form an
island. Its top was almost level and grown over with a spongy
grass, soft as a spring mattress, an ideal place for our picnics,
and also a good observation post for the weather. I'd not risk
bringing *Amanda* close into the rocks, but anchor her in deep
water about fifty yards out. I'd push the dinghy out from the
rocks on a trip anchor.

By her own choice Marie would stay on the island, writing her letters, reading, or just blissfully lazing in the sun: and we'd join her there when the tide flowed, make our fire clear of the grass and, if we'd been lucky, have a crab salad for tea.

But my weather eye would never close, and in particular I would watch the rocks at the extreme point of Pencarrow Head for the gleam of a breaking wave which might be the prelude to a rising ground swell and a change of wind. To be caught even with a moderate south-wester on the Lantivet side of the Head would not be a pleasant experience, and no matter how happy we had been, I was never really sorry when we were under way for home, to see Fowey lighthouse and the harbour mouth ahead, Pencarrow astern.

XXIV

YET THE loveliest of all our coastal landing places was Pridmouth Bay, sheltered from the south-west by Gribbin Head, to
which it bore the same physical relationship as Lantivet did to
Pencarrow. There, if the wind did come, it would be a shorter
and safer run for home, for it would be with us, and if anything
went wrong with the engine we could use the sail and oars.

Gribbin Head, which with its outlying reef the Cannis (of
double dramatic memory), formed the eastern extremity of
wide St. Austell Bay, was not so high or rugged as Pencarrow.
Its cliffs partly wooded, had a gentle slope towards Pridmouth
where they came down almost to sea level to form two beaches
of hard level sand. Shorewards from one of the beaches was the
valley of a brook which ran down from the woods of Daphne's
Menabilly, the Manderly of *Rebecca*. The brook formed a
shallow lake, fringed with bullrushes and wild irises close to
the shore and there was a clump of tall dark-foliaged cypress
trees near its banks.

Although Marie patriotically maintained that there were
places in the Western Isles to beat this, I knew of nothing in
Great Britain or on the coasts of the Mediterranean or those of
Africa and America I had visited to match Pridmouth in its
beauty on a summer's day. It was a place to drive a water-
colour painter looney, and if I was not a water-colour painter, I
had the frustrated inborn instincts of one. Wherever you looked
there was a subject for a picture, the curve of the twin beaches,
the rocks, the fields of ripening corn that sloped down into the
valley, the lone pines, the Menabilly Woods, the contrasting
blue of sky and sea.

There were no motor roads into Pridmouth. To get to it

you had either to walk along the clifftops or come by boat. The beaches were never crowded. The holidaymakers who were there in no way detracted from its beauty. The summer frocks of the women, the parasols, the gay bathing tents, the swimsuits of the bathers, their sunburnt limbs, especially those of the children, could have inspired a Renoir painting.

With now only eight days of the holidays to go we dropped anchor in Pridmouth Bay one afternoon, pulled ashore in the dinghy and carried our picnic things up to high water mark of the beach nearer to the Gribbin. The tides were still spring, but had passed their maximum. We were on the ebb, and as usual I took the precaution of pushing the dinghy well out on a trip anchor.

We'd had an early lunch and had set out before hearing the one o'clock weather forecast. The early one, however, had repeated what had become the familiar formula: "an anti-cyclone is stationary over the British Isles. The weather will continue fine and warm. Winds light and variable."

There was indeed no wind at all. The sky was cloudless, the sea calm to the horizon, a poor day for craft whose only means of propulsion was sail. What yachts were in sight were either moving with their auxiliary engines or becalmed, their sails flapping. The sun was almost tropical in its intensity. We hid our milk and butter in the shade of an overhanging rock and piled wet seaweed over them. The children lost no time in getting into the water.

Sand has its special delights for children. They can move on it in their bare feet without discomfort. They can make pies, with bucket and spade, build castles, houses, ornament them with shells, but Shawn, still at the bucket and spade age, was at the point of learning to swim, and ironically it was the other children, including Ann, who did the castle building in between swims. Marie, an expert swimmer herself, had to admit that so far as bathing was concerned Pridmouth scored over her Bonnie Scotland. She had never known the sea so warm.

And the rocks here, if not quite on such a grand scale as those of Lantivet were just as fascinating. It didn't seem to matter that in their quest for treasures there was competition from other children. Certainly it was with an air of superiority that Simon addressed another boy who was proudly holding a small spider-crab he had caught.

"Jolly good. It's a bit on the small size though. I got a real lobster the other day! And my sister actually caught a huge salmon!"

Swimming, climbing the rocks, looking for treasures, they were all as happy as ever, living in the present, as children do, yet forging more memories. Perhaps they were not conscious of the beauty of this place. Perhaps they would have been just as happy at Southend-on-Sea, or fishing for tiddlers in the Serpentine, or paddling in a muddy village duck-pond. But I could not believe that subconsciously at least, they were not taking things in, the shapes and colours of the rocks and beaches, the salty smells, the feel of the sun on their bodies, the sound of gulls; all daffodils for remembrance.

I was not so happy however that perfect afternoon. Only eight more days were left. If only time could stand still, or better still move backwards, so that I could be waiting at the station again for the arrival of their train, instead of contemplating its inevitable departure.

But I kept these gloomy thoughts to myself. The hours of the day moved inexorably on. The tide turned. Tea-time came. We gathered bits of wood for our fire, scarcer here than on the less frequented beaches of Lantic and Lantivet. We'd caught no crabs, but we'd brought yesterday's catch of prawns with us, lashings of egg-and-tomato sandwiches, cos lettuces from the garden, buns and a cake that Marie had made. The sun was still so hot that we had to eat our meal in the shade of the rock, which curtailed our view of the coast, and it was only when I got up to put some more water in the tea kettle that I glanced seawards and observed that there was a darkish patch along the horizon, that a big yacht which had been becalmed was moving shorewards with her sails filled, and heeling over to port. A breeze had sprung up, and it was from the east.

I was not at first unduly alarmed. In fine hot weather like this it was a common occurrence to get a sudden off-sea thermal wind which might just as suddenly die away. But I watched that dark patch, saw that it was spreading shorewards and that where the yacht was sailing it was flecked white. Their meal quickly finished, the children were rushing back to the tide's edge which now was advancing to the castle they had built, flooding its moat with little waves. There had been no waves at all when, with the tide ebbing, they had built it.

Those waves, they were very small, might have been caused by one of the pleasure speed-boats (most of them ex-R.A.F. launches) which ran between the resorts of Looe, Polperro, Fowey and Mevagissey. None of them was in sight however, and my apprehension became real when I felt the first puff of wind, definitely east, a head wind for our return to the harbour.

There had been two day cabin cruisers anchored in the bay when we had arrived, their dinghys on the beach. These had already departed, but probably only because their owners had to keep to their hotel or boarding-house schedule of meals. Was I being too fussy, too daddy lumpsuckerish? A wave, not big, but certainly bigger than the one that had filled the moat of the sand castle, overwhelmed it; I saw that both *Amanda* and the dinghy were rocking gently at their anchors. I made what I knew was going to be an unpopular decision.

"Come on, kids, we've got to pack up for home."

There was a chorus of protests.

"We don't want to go home yet."

"We've just come!"

"What's the hurry? It's lovely here, Daddy, do wait a bit longer!"

"It isn't bed-time yet." This from Shawn, who was making a valiant effort to be completely water-borne with Marie holding his chin.

I was adamant.

"Come on. The wind's getting up and it's east and it will soon be too chilly for bathing here. It will be all right for bathing at home. Better dry yourselves too and dress. It will be a cold trip back."

Marie, who had been swimming herself, had to drag Shawn furiously resisting out of the water. While she was drying and dressing him I hauled in the dinghy. We embarked and pulled out to *Amanda*, and by now the whole of the sea away from the bay was flecked white with the rising wind. It was not a gale, or as yet anything near one. There was still no sign of it being a prelude to the anticipated break in the weather. The sky was cloudless. There was no real swell, only what inshore boatmen call a "chop", short, steep waves with creaming tops.

Simon and Patrick elected to stay in the dinghy and fish. They were still hopeful of emulating Ann and her salmon trout. Pretending that it was only to protect them from the wind— they were very thinly clad—I made them put on their kapok life-jackets however. It was routine that Shawn should wear his. I saw that the dinghy painter was secure. Then, with *Amanda's* anchor still down, I turned on the petrol, flooded the carburettor, gave the starting handle a swing. Nothing happened. I looked at the magneto switch. It was on. I gave the handle a more vigorous swing. Still nothing happened. I reached into the cabin for my tool box, found the plug spanner, cleaned the points of all four plugs, tested them for spark, put them back and tried the handle again. The engine was still dead.

"Is there any petrol in the tank?" Simon shouted from the dinghy.

What motorist or motor boat owner has not been caught out when trying to start a dead engine by this simple omission? I knew that the tank was at least half full, but I looked to make sure. The carburettor was flooding anyway. The trouble must be a choked jet. There were three of these devices: one at the top of the carburettor and fairly easy to remove, the other two at its base. To get at these I had to remove the engine box, crouch down, unscrew two nuts and insert a special tool that gripped the jet ends and allowed them to be unscrewed. I blew through each of the jets, screwed them back, all the time trying not to think of what might happen if I couldn't start the engine at all.

We were still partly in the lee of the rocks that reached seawards from the bay and already *Amanda* was pitching and rolling. The flood tide would be in our favour, but even if the wind got no stronger than it was at present, I would not be able to make headway against it with the oars. The sail, of course, would be completely useless. And the wind was definitely freshening. If it increased to only a stiff breeze we'd be on a rocky lee-shore, our only hope that some powerful motor boat on its way to Fowey might see us and give us a tow.

I put back the engine box. I seized the starting handle, and swung with all my might. The engine back-fired, the handle flying out of my hand. Momentarily I was nonplussed. Then remembering that this had once happened before, I looked at the plug leads, traced them to the magneto and found I had mixed them when I had put the plugs back after cleaning. I changed them to their right places and with a silent Christian Humanist prayer, gave the handle another swing. The engine started. There was a chorus of "Hooray" from the children. I sprang up on to the fore deck, hauled up the anchor, then back to the tiller, put the engine ahead and steered out for the open sea.

I had on several occasions when on my own proved that *Amanda* was a good sea boat when under way and meeting the waves head on. She would throw the water and spray even of a breaking wave clear of the hull. But anchored or drifting she would roll uncomfortably even with a slight swell, and she certainly did some rolling until we were clear of the rocks and I turned her into the weather.

But it was the first time the children had been in *Amanda*

in anything but a dead calm sea. I wouldn't have been surprised if they had been scared. Instead they were thrilled, and Ann was indignant when I insisted that she should not be in her usual place on the foredeck. But they all shouted with glee as we crashed into and over the waves as though we were riding on a scenic railway at a fair; and looking astern I observed that Simon and Patrick were equally happy in the pitching dinghy, that they had both got their lines overboard.

There was no actual danger in these waves. I could have been as happy myself if I had known with complete certainty that there was no possibility of the engine stalling before we were through the harbour mouth, still a mile away. If it did, we would be in a worse fix than ever. There were several yachts and motor boats in sight, but none near enough to signal to. I listened to the throbbing of the engine with the same intensity as I had once done to the sound of our aeroplane engine when flying over the African jungle on a war reconnaissance. A "miss," an unusual vibration, a change in the "tune," would bring my heart into my mouth.

We hadn't got as far as Coombe when both Simon and Patrick shouted at the same time:

"Fish! Fish!"

We saw them excitedly hauling in, and then lift a couple of nice mackerel aboard.

The vast shoals of mackerel had never reappeared, but on our various trips we had caught odd ones, and medium-sized pollack when trolling. All the children, including Shawn, were now expert at handling lines, bait and fish.

Our usual practice when a fish was caught by trolling was to put about and troll as near as possible to where the fish was hooked. The boys had already put their lines over again, and Simon yelled:

"Aren't we going to turn? It might be a shoal."

He didn't know how anxiously I was looking ahead, measuring the slowly diminishing gap between ourselves and safety. He hadn't seen what I had seen with a deeper alarm, that the storm cone was hoisted on the coastguard's flagstaff on the top of Polruan cliff. I didn't turn, and as both of them had hooked fish again there was no more questioning except that Shawn cried rather indignantly that it was his turn to fish. Couldn't he and Henrietta change places with Simon and Patrick? What a hope!

The wind was increasing, the waves getting steeper. I daren't open the throttle to full. The dinghy was yawing too, helping to retard our speed. It seemed to me hours before we got abreast of Coombe, and Simon and Patrick were still hauling the mackerel in, the others shrieking with delight whenever we encountered an extra big wave. Marie too seemed to be enjoying it. The big yacht, her mainsail lowered, was now in the lee of Polruan cliff passing into the harbour. Several motor boats coming from the east were speeding in out of the weather, and we had still a quarter of a mile to go. I tried to keep my eyes averted from the jagged rocks at the foot of Fowey cliff, white with foam. If the engine stalled now, only a miracle could stop us being blown into them.

"They've stopped biting," Simon yelled. "Can't we go back just for a bit? It must have been a shoal."

"Do let's," yelled Patrick. "It's the best fishing we've had yet."

I sympathised with them. But ruthlessly I carried on, pretending I hadn't heard them. We were drawing abreast of the lighthouse, less than a hundred yards from the foam-fringed castle point. I steered seawards a little for the opposite cliff of Polruan, and I think I must have held my breath as we passed the lighthouse, reached the point, opening up the entire harbour, its surface ruffled with the wind, but level and safe. I kept on however until we were beyond mid-channel, the waves if anything steeper, but the wind falling as we neared the cliff. And then I put the helm over. We ran in, close to the foot of Polruan Castle, to smooth water. Only then did I turn round to look at the dinghy. And I said with a nonchalance that I certainly didn't feel:

"Haul in your lines now. How many did you get?"

"Gosh!" Simon answered. "We haven't had time to count them. At least twenty. There must have been a terrific shoal. When can we go back? It isn't really rough!"

Where ignorance is bliss . . . I looked at the cone on the coastguard's flagstaff, at the shaking trees on the rising ground above the town of Fowey, at the wisps of cloud now scudding across the sky from the sea, and again I said nuthin' and lay low. No words indeed could have expressed what I was feeling as with *Amanda* now on a level keel, and her ancient engine purring like a well-fed cat, I steered up the harbour for home.

XXV

Was it the break? We were too late to get the six o'clock news and weather forecast. It was now nearly high water. The trees on the skyline above the creek on the opposite side to the cove were shaking more violently than those at Fowey. The surface of the creek was furred with twisting gusts, but there were no waves. The cove, completely sheltered, was as smooth as if there had been no wind at all and as soon as we landed the children were in the water again, Shawn determined that before bedtime he was going to finish his lessons which had been so rudely interrupted, and actually swim.

Even with the ragged clouds scudding across the sky and occasionally obscuring the lowering sun, it was still hot, still a summer day, or rather evening. It might be the break but it might not. At sunset the wind might fall, and there might be nothing but a little ground swell outside the harbour in the morning. We'd know when we got the nine o'clock news.

Grilled mackerel for supper, new potatoes, and peas straight from the garden! I cleaned and filleted the mackerel myself on the beach of the cove, all the time keeping my eyes on Shawn who had refused all offers of help and had waded in over his waist. He was crouching down, facing the beach, moving his arms and hands in the correct method of the breast stroke, but his feet still apparently touching bottom. I knew what was in his mind, that instinctive reluctance to leave go and kick out.

I said nothing, pretending I wasn't watching. But I saw him take a deep breath, blowing out his cheeks, then kick out frantically with arms and legs, and definitely move towards the beach, until he grounded in the shallows, when he stood up, panting but triumphant.

I dropped the fish I was cleaning, waded in and hugged him.

"I swum! I swum!" he gasped. "I swum. Watch me do it again!"

There was no need to wait for the nine o'clock news. While we were having supper the skies darkened, and for the first time in the holiday there was the patter of rain on the roof. When I went out it was to discover that the wind had veered to south-west and was blowing half a gale straight up the creek, that *Amanda* was pitching at her mooring, well out in the creek itself.

Henrietta was putting the still triumphant Shawn to bed. Now that he could really swim, would he have to go on wearing his life-jacket when he was in *Amanda*, he had asked me when I had said good night to him. Ann was going to help Marie wash up before settling down to her book. Wearing their raincoats, Simon and Patrick came down with me to the cove. I wanted to assure myself that both boats were secure for the night.

How different the cove looked now in the rain and the growing storm. It was hard to believe that this had been so calm and sunny and warm for more than three weeks; that we had sun-bathed on the shingle, where the children had made fires and boiled winkles, and had their aquarium. It was at least an hour past the official time of high tide. There was no sign yet of the ebb. The wind was holding up the coastal tidal current. The water was actually lapping the third of the concrete steps, and although we were completely sheltered from the wind, there were waves in the cove.

I had made a secure permanent mooring for *Amanda* with double bridled anchors, buried deep in the mud, with a swivel and chain leading through a fairlead on her stem to the base of her mast. The dinghy was fastened to an endless line called an "out-haul," locally known as a "frape." The line ran through two pulleys, one fixed to an anchorage at the mud edge of the shingle, the other fixed ashore close to the steps. It was the same principle as the device used by the Life-Saving Rocket Brigade for hauling in the breeches buoy between the shore and a wrecked ship.

The dinghy was now riding half-way out to *Amanda* and in the lee of the cove cliff. We hauled her in to the steps. I was in some doubt about taking the boys with me. They had left their life-jackets in *Amanda* when we came ashore. But I mustn't be too fussy, too "daddy lumperish." I gave them the choice. They jumped in without hesitation and I let Simon pull until we were out of the lee of the cliff and into the wind.

There was no real danger, yet I rightly guessed that the wind was too strong for him to make even the short distance still separating us from *Amanda*, although he made a valiant effort before surrendering the oars and joining Patrick in the stern. It was not a full gale yet. The surface waves were short and steep as they had been when we had turned out of the shelter of Pridmouth, but under them was the longer swell of the big combers breaking on the cliffs of the harbour mouth which was now in sight.

The boys were impressed.

"Gosh! Just look at the breakers," said Simon. "It's a jolly good job we did come back when we did."

"Daddy," I said ironically, "occasionally knows best."

"I don't think that I'd like to be fishing outside the harbour now," said Patrick, adding a little nervously, "We're all right here, though, aren't we?"

I assured him that we were; this was the creek, not the open sea.

I was pulling on a slanting course, into the waves in order to get to windward of *Amanda* before closing her, and I had to use all my strength to do so. I was about a length ahead when I shipped the oars, and as the wind and waves took charge and brought her alongside, I made a grab at one of the stays, and made the dinghy's painter fast. Both boats were now bucking and cavorting like two restive horses, or rather a horse and foal.

It was a tricky job changing mounts. I had to warn the boys to watch out they didn't get their hands caught between the two gunwales. Once in *Amanda* I could take stock of the situation.

We were safe of course. The swivel on the mooring chain allowed her to keep head on to wind and waves. Temporarily the rain had stopped. The sky, however, was completely overcast, and it was through the veil of an approaching rain squall that we saw the huge waves smashing along the whole of the Fowey sea-front from the castle to the ferry breakwater. We saw the ferry-boat itself pitching and rolling heavily, taking an unusual course up-harbour for the relatively smooth approaches of the Town Quay. All the other craft in the crowded harbour were pitching and rolling, straining at their anchors, and suddenly I spotted the big launch in which Arthur had first landed me at the cove moving close to two big anchored yachts which, with their anchors apparently dragging, and oilskinned men hurrying about their decks, seemed on the point of colliding. It looked as though Arthur himself was at the tiller of the launch, that he was engaged on one of his emergency salvage jobs.

Was it La Rochefoucauld who said there is always something a little pleasing to us in the misfortunes even of our dearest friends? Subconsciously at least it is with a mingled horror and satisfaction, that it hasn't happened to us, that we read or hear of or witness other people's disasters. There is a bond, a brotherhood between all men who "go down to the sea in ships" whether they do it for their livelihood or for pleasure, whether their "ships" be large or small or merely little boats. We help others when trouble comes to them, and expect it for ourselves. I could, and indeed did, feel a sympathy with the owners of the two yachts, but I could not repress a pleasurable excitement at what I saw, and my sons were shamelessly enjoying the spectacle, even, I suspected, hoping that the yachts would collide and even sink. The launch, and I was certain that its occupant was Arthur, had got a line on to the yacht on the weather side to tow it clear. But before we could tell if he had succeeded the squall obliterated the whole of the harbour. It roared up the creek whipping the crests of the waves into spray, and bringing with it a torrential downpour of rain.

There was no point in the boys getting drenched. I made them shelter in the cabin while I checked the mooring chain, and then worked the bilge pump until it sucked dry. With heavy continuous rain on top of her slow leak there was a risk of the bilge rising to the level of the magneto. There was nothing more I could do.

Despite that the wind was now reaching gale force, that the waves were growing steeper, I knew that there was still no danger, but I took the precaution of asking the boys to put on their life-jackets, and again I exercised caution in superintending their re-embarkation into the pitching dinghy. When they were safely seated in the stern, I got in myself, saw that the oars were ready, then cast off, waiting until the wind and waves had moved us clear, then started pulling slightly to windward of the cove. She was a splendid boat. I'd have felt safe in her in almost any sort of weather, safer indeed than in *Amanda*, for there was no engine to worry about, and I must have conveyed my confidence to the boys, for they laughed when a wave broke over her bow drenching me with spray. But with less than a score of strokes and the beam wind if anything helping, I reached the lee of the cove, and moved easily into the steps.

We got out and I fastened the dinghy to the frape. The boys hauled it out. The rain was pelting down vertically where we stood, almost horizontally up the creek, with the spray whipped from the waves making a curtain through which *Amanda* was just visible, riding bravely. A premature dusk was falling too.

"Come on," I said, "let's get up to the house and change."

The boys took my hands, one on each side as we walked up the path, and Simon said, completely out of the blue:

"We've only got eight days left before we have to go home, haven't we?"

"Yes," I said, "only eight days," and it was on my lips to say, "Are you sorry?" but it would have been a leading question. I sensed that Simon was battling with a double loyalty. Throughout their stay I had stuck meticulously to the bargain that I would never discuss our broken marriage with any of the children. I had never mentioned their mother's or Bertha's name. I'd asked them no questions about their home. My wife had written to them all regularly, sent them presents. They had written to her, perhaps not so regularly and with an undoubted reluctance, for children hate writing letters, and I did not take this as a sign of any lessening of their affection for her, which would have given me no satisfaction. I had as meticulously refrained from reading any of these letters, either hers or theirs, which would have been easy, for they were not secretive about them. Yet I was not prepared for Simon's next remark:

"I wouldn't mind living here altogether, Daddy. I like living by the sea, and bathing and fishing, and having boats. Gosh! it was exciting hauling those mackerel in. I'd like to live here for always."

"I would too," said Patrick, "but only if Mummy came too. Marie's all right, but she's not our mummy, is she?"

Once more I lay low and said nuthin'. We were getting near the house and Henrietta, always the little mother, was rushing down to meet us, a coat over her head:

"Hey! Where have you all been? You must be wet through. Don't say you've been fishing again in a storm like this. It's long past your bedtime too!"

"Don't make such a fuss," Simon said airily. "We've just been out to *Amanda* to see that she's all right. Someone's got to do it, haven't they? We're all right, aren't we, Daddy?"

And with both my boys holding my hands tightly, we carried on to the house, following Henrietta to the open door.

"Yes," I said, with the words they had spoken ringing in my ears. "*We're* all right."

It was a noisy night. Although we were protected from the

full force of the gale, I could hear it roaring up the creek. It never stopped raining and the stream in flood was a miniature Niagara. I stayed, trying to read by the light of a Tilly lamp, in the big room until the tide had ebbed. Then in oilskins and thigh boots I went down to the cove, to find the beach piled deep with seaweed and debris, including some of the planks of a dinghy, a mooring buoy, and a single oar. It was with relief that my flashlight revealed our own dinghy and *Amanda* herself safely aground on the mud.

The dinghy was half full of water. I took out the plug, and now exposed to the gale, I made my way to the edge of the mud. The swollen stream had scoured a deep channel through the shingle. Although *Amanda* was aground there was still water in the creek which varied in depth as the wash of the big broken and dissipated sea waves flooded in and then receded, leaving the mud temporarily exposed.

The mud itself was about a foot deep between the edge of the shingle and the mooring. Normally, and in daylight, one had to be expert in negotiating it, for it had a terrific suction on one's feet. You had to keep moving, and wriggle your foot to loosen it before drawing out at a slant for the next step, and always keep the pressure even. Now with the gale buffeting me, and the water alternately swirling up and then back again, it was a devil of a job. Just before I reached *Amanda* an extra big wash came in and catching me off my balance nearly knocked me over. I saved myself by leaning over and seizing her gunwale, but when as the wash receded I tried to haul myself on board, one of my feet would not budge and I had to draw it out of the boot itself, which promptly filled with water.

But I was on board, and as I shone the lamp inside I saw that I had just come in time. The water was well above the floorboards, and actually touching the base of the magneto, and the rain was still pelting down. It would take at least twenty minutes to pump her dry again, and by then the tide would certainly be flowing. I might have to swim for the shore or remain on board till morning. Luckily there was a bucket in the cabin. I took out the bottom boards near the stern and baled furiously.

I hadn't finished when a big wash came in. This time *Amanda* was afloat, definite proof that the tide had turned, for when it receded the mud did not bare at all. She was nearly dry, however. Hurriedly I tried to put on the boot I had pulled out of the mud—tried—but discovered that my foot would not move past the tight-fitting ankle joint. Another wash was coming in. In despair I pulled off the other boot, and with only stockings on my feet, got over the side and started for the shore, losing one of my stockings before I reached the shingle.

The children would have been highly amused if they could have seen me, "one sock off and one sock on," hobbling gingerly over the sharp-edged pebbles. I was putting the bilge cork back in the dinghy, when there was a sudden flash, like sheet lightning, in the storm clouds overhead, and within a fraction of a second, a loud report. In less than a minute there was another flash, another explosion. I had lived too long by the sea not to know the meaning of those sounds. They were the summoning signals for the lifeboat crew and despite the incontrovertible wisdom of Monsieur La Rochefoucauld and that my first reaction was a gladness that I and my family were not involved, my finer instincts were as instantly aroused, and predominated. If there was a prayer in orthodox Christian usage that could shake my disbelief in the existence of God, it was the singing of the hymn:

> Eternal Father, strong to save,
> Whose arm doth bind the restless wave,
> Who bidd'st the mighty ocean deep
> Its own appointed limits keep:
>> O hear us when we cry to Thee
>> For those in peril on the sea!

The Fowey motor lifeboat, of the most modern type, was permanently afloat on moorings close to the Town Quay. There was a salaried engineer who lived close by whose duties were to see to her maintenance and readiness for duty. The voluntary coxswain, a second engineer, and crew, all experienced seafarers, lived on the Fowey side of the harbour, and they'd be tumbling out of their beds before the sound of the second maroon.

From here, except for those dramatic sounds, there was no clue to what was happening. The roar of the lifeboat's twin engines starting would be drowned by the sound of wind and breakers. Visibility, with the rain and spray and the darkness of night, was next to nil. I was impotent. I moved on up the steps and path to the shelter and security of my home; but I was praying in my heart if not in my mind that those in trouble, the distressed and the rescuers, whoever they were, would come to no harm.

XXVI

DAYBREAK brought no easing of the storm. I hadn't been to bed.
I'd snatched a little sleep on the settee in the big room before
making one more strenuous trip to *Amanda* to bale out the
water. As soon as it was daylight I climbed up the path above
the house to a point where I had a view over the gale-swept
middle harbour. I was mystified and relieved to see that the
lifeboat was at its moorings. There were fewer craft in the
harbour than there had been last night. Many of them, including the two big yachts, must have moved to the shelter of the
upper river. It was too early in the morning for the ferry to
be running. Tremendous waves were smashing over the breakwater of the Fowey ferry landing, so when it did start it
would have to embark and disembark its passengers at the
Station Quay.

Only seven more days to go! And now it seemed it was
already "good-bye" to summer. But what fears I had that the
children were going to be miserable to find the sun no longer
shining were quickly dispelled. The storm, the firing of the
lifeboat maroons, apparently had not disturbed their slumbers.
They couldn't wait for breakfast, but dashed straight out of
the house, clad only in their bathing garments, to marvel first
at the roaring flooded stream, then to run down to the sheltered
cove, where yesterday they had taken their first dip in the
crystal clear sunlit water. Temporarily it had stopped raining
although the gale was strong as ever.

The tide was higher than it had been at its maximum last
night. Where normally at the highest of spring tides the water
would have been only ankle deep at the steps, there was now at
least four feet; the primrose plants (flowerless of course) were

awash and so were the ends of some of the overhanging branches of the oaks. And the water itself, stained with the flood water from the stream and river, was the colour of strong cocoa.

For once the elder children were not tempted to dive in. The surface of the cove was almost entirely covered with floating weed—a Sargasso Sea in miniature, with a further accumulation of marine and fresh-water debris, dead branches which must have come down with the flooded river, odd planks, the engine-box of a motor boat, bottom boards, another mooring buoy, and two more oars, which we were able to fish out with a long bamboo.

It was Shawn who was the first to complain. He wanted to prove again that he could really swim, and he was furious that I wouldn't even let him paddle on the top step over which the waves were washing if not actually breaking.

"The water's too deep," I said. "You'll have to wait till the tide goes down."

"But I can swim, I can swim," he protested. "It doesn't matter if it *is* deep."

"Don't be silly," Simon said, "*I* wouldn't like to try and swim with all that seaweed about."

"And the water's so dirty," put in Henrietta, who had firmly grasped Shawn's hand as a precaution.

"Are we going to pull out to *Amanda* again?" Simon asked, with bravado I thought, for although the dinghy was riding easily among the sea-weed in the cove, *Amanda* was pitching wildly at her mooring.

We could have done it. I could tell by her water-line, however, that her bilge was within safe limits, and I said no. It was breakfast-time. Another rain squall was advancing up the creek. Although Ann and Patrick were excitedly trying to fish the engine-box ashore, they were all in their bathing things and I was parentally responsible. But as I gave the word for retreat there was the sound of a motor, and the ferry launch, with oilskinned Arthur at the tiller, came in sight round the bluff of the cove riding the waves of the squall.

He waved to us, steered in, stopped alongside the dinghy and made fast to her. The children had met him several times, shared my liking for him.

"Ahoy!" he shouted. "What do you make of this? Are you all right? I see that *Amanda's* taking it well, riding it handsome. You haven't seen any paddles or bottom boards, have 'e? My dinghy's filled at her mooring and everything that floats has washed out of her."

The children excitedly held up the oars they had hauled ashore.

Arthur grinned.

"That's a bit of luck. But I guessed I'd find 'em here with the wind sou'west. And I see that's an engine-box belonging to a pal of mine. His boat's sunk, but that's nothing to what's happened over at Fowey. What a night, eh?" He was slowly hauling his boat and our dinghy in towards the steps. "Did you hear the lifeboat gun?"

"What happened, Arthur?"

"There was hell to play! Know that big yawl *Black Maria*? She dragged her moorings, drifted in to Fowey Town Quay, right among all the dinghys and yachts, dragged them along with her until she fetched up on the lifeboat and nearly rammed her with her bowsprit. Getting them all clear was a bigger job for the lifeboat coxswain and crew than they've ever had outside the harbour. I don't know how many small craft were sunk or damaged. There'll be enough repair jobs to keep every boat yard busy the rest of the summer, and the gale's not over yet."

"It must have been exciting," Simon said wistfully. "I wish I'd seen it."

"And me," said Patrick.

I did myself, but I didn't say so.

They handed him the paddles. He looked at the planks still floating among the weed. He did not recognise any of his own bottom boards. I asked him if he would like to come up to the house and have a cup of coffee.

"Thanks, but I've too many jobs to do, although it's my

morning off the ferry, and I want to run up to the end of the creek and see if I can find them bottom boards of mine. You get in out of the rain."

He sheered off, steering up creek, and was soon out of sight.

It was pelting down again. We hurried up to the house, Shawn now crying with vexation. He wanted the sun to shine. He hated the wind and the rain and the rough sea and everything that stopped him from having a swim. I had prepared myself for this. I hugged him.

"Don't worry, Shawn," I said, "I've got a big surprise for you, something that's going to please you very much, a super super present."

We had reached the shelter of the veranda.

"What *is* it?" he demanded tearfully.

"You can all have a thousand guesses, but you'll have to wait till we've had breakfast until you see it."

"Is it animal, vegetable or mineral?" Simon asked.

"Mineral," I said.

Shawn was cheering up.

"Is it just for me? Is it a tricycle? I do want a tricycle. Is it just for me?"

"It isn't a tricycle, and it isn't just for you, but you're going to like it, for it isn't exactly an 'it,' it's a whole lot of 'its'."

"Breakfast's ready!" Marie called from the kitchen.

The guessing game went on while we polished off the rest of the mackerel, but none got anywhere near the answer. Breakfast over, I called for a general assembly in the big room, and I built up the suspense further by getting the children to help move all the furniture into one corner and fold up the carpet, leaving the bare linoleum. Then from my bedroom where I had kept them hidden I fetched the three big cardboard boxes, still tied up with string and planted them in the middle of the room.

"Here we are," I said. "Who's going to open them?"

I could see that Ann and Henrietta were as excited as the

boys were, that even Marie was enjoying the drama of the situation. The pelting rain on the roof, the gale-lashed creek, were forgotten.

"It's just like Christmas morning," laughed Ann. "Let the boys do it. Come on, Shawn, make a start. Shall I help you untie the knots?"

One of the boxes was bigger than the others. It was natural but unfortunate that Shawn should pick on it. He reluctantly accepted Ann's assistance with the knots, waving her to stand clear as he opened the flaps and pulled out a bundle of track sections. He looked at them with disgust.

"What *are* they? I don't want things like this!"

He dropped them on the floor and hauled out another bundle. Then Patrick gave an excited shout as he lifted from his box a model locomotive.

"Look at this!" he cried, "look at this!"

He held it up. It was an exact replica of the real thing, strongly built, complete with bogie wheels and a detachable tender; it even had a polished brass ring round its squat funnel, the symbol of the express.

"Isn't it absolutely smashing!" he cried, then aware of Shawn's discomfiture he said generously, "Come on, you have it. I think there's another. Don't you see what it is? It's a model railway. Those are the rails in your box!"

"Gosh! and look here," Simon shouted. "A signal box. A bridge. Carriages. Trucks . . ."

Although I had been given a detailed catalogue of the contents of the boxes I had never opened them. The person who had sold the "set" to me was a widow, and she had told me in a pathetic letter that it had belonged to her only son, and a cousin of his own age, both of whom had been killed in the war. It had taken them years of their schoolboy pocket money to acquire the various items. If they had lived to have children of their own it would have gone to them, although they might have thought it a bit old-fashioned to have clock-work engines, instead of electric. Her boy and his cousin had

had many happy hours playing with it. It kept them out of mischief too. She and her sister, the mother of the other boy, had been a long time making up their minds to sell it, but they had felt that it wasn't right to keep it packed away when it might be giving pleasure to other children.

If only the widow and her sister could have been here now to see the faces of my own children as they greeted each new discovery; three more locomotives; two complete passenger trains; a goods train; a station; a crane; a water-tank complete with rubber hose; points, switches.

Ann and Henrietta, as enthusiastic as the boys, were fitting the track sections together. Most of them were straight, some were curved. There were enough of them to make a continuous circuit of the whole room. But the boys couldn't wait. They were winding up the engines and trying them on the bare floor. How fortunate it was, I thought, that I'd had that floor made level. The most powerful of the locomotives, even without carriages or trucks attached could not have climbed that original slant which had made us give odd legs to our furniture when we had first made this our home.

The boxes at last were empty. The single track completed, with switches and double tracks laid for the station. Marie unostentatiously had moved back into the kitchen. I waited until I had seen the first passenger train, which included a restaurant coach and guards van go full pelt round the room, then I joined Marie in the kitchen to help her wash up the breakfast things.

"Well," I said, "what do you make of my idea of catering for a rainy day?"

She laughed dryly.

"A master stroke," she said. "Bribery, if not corruption, and I don't know whether it's quite fair to your wife. You're a skilful fisherman, aren't you, Leo—a connoisseur of baits."

"The bait's not just for them, dear Marie."

"I know what you mean; 'a sprat to catch a mackerel, a mackerel to catch a whale.' You're giving them a good time

195

anyway. It's a heavenly place this. They'll want to come again, of course." Then she said: "I'm still strictly neutral," and added with convincing sincerity, "I only hope you do catch your whale."

Five days—four days—three days—two days—one day—a ghastly count-down.

Although there were no more gales, the weather had definitely broken. "Showers and bright intervals, winds variable, light to moderate, further outlook unsettled," had replaced in the radio forecasts what for so long had been the monotonous prediction of continuing anti-cyclonic conditions. The light and variable winds were strong enough and southerly enough in direction to prevent the heavy swell left by the gale from dying down. Landing at any of the coastal coves would have been a risky operation.

Yet the sun in those "bright intervals" was as hot as ever. The showers when they came were not heavy enough to cause even a staining of the water in the stream. That in the creek changed from cocoa brown to tea, and then light wine, and finally to its usual crystal clarity.

We had cleared all the cast-up sea-weed from the beach of the cove, making a huge heap of this above the steps which later I could transfer to the garden to make a compost. Bathing at least was back to normal during those so rapidly receding days. Having mastered the breast stroke, Shawn was making a valiant effort to do the crawl, an art that I had never been able to master myself. When it rained however he had been blissfully happy with the railway.

The prawns, seasonal in their habits, had vanished. The boys had tried bottom fishing in the creek and harbour with only moderate success. But on this last afternoon we had dug a tin of lugworms and baited a long hundred hook line which we had shot in deep water clear of the steamship fairway to the jetties. Marked with a buoy at each end and well anchored, we had left it and pulled over to Fowey for a final round of ice creams, and to call at the club for the boys to make their farewells to Wilfred. Ann and Henrietta were helping Marie in the dismal job of packing.

Fishing with a set line is not angling. Hauling it can be just as exciting, for you never know what you are going to catch. It has the advantage of covering a large area of the bottom, whereas when fishing with hand-lines from an anchored boat the area is scarcely bigger than the boat itself. It has the disadvantage that the baits *are* on the bottom, out of control, and more likely to be devoured by crabs or starfish before the real fish spot them.

Simon was to do the actual hauling. The others could look over the side, and see the hooks and whatever was on them coming up. First, however, having picked up the first buoy, he had to haul in the anchor line, which of course had no hooks on it. Then came the first hook on a short snood attached to the main line, spaced six feet from the next one.

He was hauling against the tide and I was at the oars, taking the strain off the line. Hook after hook came in, some bare, some with starfish still clinging to the bait. Then he shouted:

"I can feel something wriggling! I think it's a fish!"

"Perhaps it's a salmon," said Patrick who, like Simon, had never given up hope of emulating Ann's famous catch.

Salmon don't eat lugworms and in British waters at least they are not caught on set lines. I saw that the landing net was ready however as Simon went on hauling. The water although clear was much too deep to see more than four of the spaced hooks at a time as they came up, and at least another dozen were hauled in before we saw a flash of white deep down. I knew what it was, if the boys at first didn't. It was a flatfish, plaice, dab, flounder or sole, showing its white belly as it struggled to free itself from the hook.

I stood up, holding the landing net. Simon went on hauling, and soon we all saw it clearly, white one moment, pale green the next as it turned, showing the tell-tale ruby spots of a plaice. But I had never seen one half as big caught locally. The steel frame of the landing net bent as I got the weight of it and heaved it in. It was over eighteen inches from head to tail, a foot in width, thick too, in prime condition. And as I despatched it and took it off the hook, I had a sudden inspiration. To appreciate the full flavour of plaice, they must not be eaten fresh but kept for at least a couple of days in the larder or 'fridge. This one if carefully gutted and packed would be a nice present for the children to take home to their mother. Undoubtedly they would give her graphic descriptions of how it was caught, unconsciously invoking more memories of our old home and the happy life we had lived.

I said nothing just then. Simon, exultant, had now handed over the hauling of the line to Patrick, for we were still only half-way to the other end. In spite of his protests, it was too tricky a job for Shawn. More bare hooks, or hooks with starfish came in, and then at last Patrick was able to shout that he could feel a wriggling. Shortly we saw the tell-tale gleam.

"It must be another plaice!" he shouted.

"I bet it's not so big as mine," said Simon.

It was not a plaice. It was not a flatfish at all. It looked like a bass, and more exciting still there were soon no less than three similar fish in sight on consecutive hooks. As the first of them came within range of the landing net, I saw that it was not a bass, for although its back was grey, its sides and belly were mottled with crimson, its head was the head of a mullet. Yet it was not until it was out of the net, flapping on the bottom boards that I knew for certain that it was indeed a red mullet, one of the rarest and most beautiful, and highly prized of all British fish; a fish indeed for epicures.

There were three of them, each weighing about two pounds, and one small flounder on the very last hook of the line, which I threw back alive into the sea. We had more than enough for our last supper, and when I suggested that they *should* take the plaice home with them there was a general enthusiastic "yes."

The last supper . . . They were catching an early train in the morning. Marie was going too and would be with them as far as Exeter. It was a gorgeous meal. The mullet, which I had filleted and Marie had fried a lovely golden brown, were delicious with a salad of lettuce from the rain-refreshed garden, cold "new" potatoes, and shallots and a home-made mayonnaise. A bramble pie, made Yorkshire fashion with crust top and bottom, warm from the oven, was the perfect dessert.

The children were all cheerful, full of high spirits as well as good food, living in the present, apparently without a thought of the morrow. I was feeling like hell myself, trying, without success, not to think that to-morrow at this time, the house would be empty.

Late that night, when everyone was in bed, I walked down the path to the cove. The wind had dropped. The tide was at half-ebb with *Amanda* just aground on the mud. The sky was clear of cloud, and mud and water and the opposite banks of the creek were lit by the waning moon. Somewhere among the trees an owl was hooting. Two swans, gleaming ghostly white in the light of the moon, were moving lazily down-creek on the ebb. I heard the plaintive cry of a curlew and in the stillness of the night the sound of an express train on the distant main line, a grim reminder of what was to happen in the morning.

And suddenly I was tempted of the devil. Why should I let it happen? Why should I let them go back? Legally and morally the children were as much mine as they were their mother's. This was a good home I had provided for them. Nothing could please me more than that she should come and share it. If she continued to refuse then I could, as much for my own convenience as for the welfare of the children, engage a permanent housekeeper. Marie, who had expressed her willingness to come next summer holidays, if by then things had not been squared up, had her own job and commitments. But it was not essential that I should have a mutual friend or have my wife vet my choice. There must be thousands of women in Great Britain who liked children, and the open-air life, who'd like to live in a place like this, who'd be thrilled by the sheer beauty of what confronted me at this moment.

What would the children say if at breakfast, when they were

all togged up in their going-away clothes, I announced to them that they were not going to catch that hated train after all? That it was bathing, boating, fishing, or if it was raining, the model train as usual.

But I wanted my wife just as much as I wanted the children. If I kept them from her, as she had kept them from me, she might construe this as an act of vengeance. She might come back but it would be under duress. It would dish for ever the possibility of a complete reconciliation.

"Softly, softly, catchee monkey!"

I'd been a good boy. I'd kept meticulously to all my promises. The children must go back in the morning. They'd had a good time. They'd talk, they'd propagand, and that fat plaice was not such a bad substitute for the *Reader's Digest* box of chocolates, or a bouquet of orchids.

XXVII

THERE had been a spell of cold weather in May while I was so busy working on the house and garden, and although the creek had often looked tempting enough I'd never risk a swim, for having little fat on my body I was very sensitive to cold. I'd been over to Fowey one day in the dinghy, and as the tide had been too low on my return to make her fast to the frape, I'd tied the painter to a clump of seaweed, thinking I'd move her when the tide flowed.

Hours must have passed when I remembered. The tide by then had flowed to the mouth of the cove and when I ran down she was not in sight. It was not until I got to the water's edge that I saw her about a hundred yards up the creek in which there was no sign of any other boat, drifting with the flood tide and the north-westerly wind, which was bitterly cold. There was a coil of light rope on the steps. The tide was lapping the foot of the banks of the creek, but it was still shallow enough there for me to wade along until I was at a point just opposite to the dinghy, now about ten yards out in deep water and still moving.

I tied a stone to the end of the line and heaved it out. It fell short. I tried again and again and with each throw became more exasperated. And it was exasperation that did it. I stripped off my clothes and, stark naked, waded in, over my knees, my thighs, my waist, until it was up to my armpits, and then I struck out, swimming, until I reached her and grasped her gunwale, and with one huge effort hauled myself aboard.

I seized the oars, pulled back to the shore for my clothes, realised the futility of trying to put them on my wet body, and bundled them into the boat, and still stark naked in the wind pulled back to the cove, tied the dinghy to the frape, and ran up to the house for a towel. And the remarkable thing was that although wind and water had been almost freezing cold, I had not for one second been aware of it. It was as though my obsession to rescue the boat had acted like an anæsthetic.

And now on the morning of departure, an event which I had dreaded, very much the same thing happened. It was torture, but I couldn't feel it. The fact that it was a perfect day again, the sky cloudless, the wind off-shore, the sea smooth, ideal for an outing along the coast did not distress me. We had breakfast. The luggage was packed, and so was the plaice. They were all in their best togs. The tide was right. Both boats were afloat, *Amanda* still with the Red Ensign flying at her mast top.

We embarked, sailed down creek and up the harbour, still crowded with yachts and pleasure craft, to the Station Quay . . . The train was waiting, not so crowded as it had been on the day of their arrival. They all got in, and I got in too, and I gave each of the children a hug, for I had disliked being kissed as a boy. I'd already expressed my gratitude to Marie. The porters started to slam the doors. I got out. The guard's whistle blew. The train moved off, with the children waving to me through the open window, and soon it was out of sight. Emotions are catching, and I think the children had reacted to my apparent nonchalance. There had been no tears.

And I walked back alone to the quay and *Amanda*. Should I strike the Red Ensign from her mast? I decided to let it stay!

BOOK THREE

Paradise Regained

I

THERE ARE several ways of curing, or at least ameliorating, that distressing condition of the human mind known romantically if not scientifically as a broken heart.

The most efficacious is suicide; but—to quote that wise poet Dorothy Parker:

> Razors pain you;
> Rivers are damp;
> Acids stain you;
> And drugs cause cramp.
> Guns aren't lawful;
> Nooses give;
> Gas smells awful;
> You might as well live.

You can take to drink or drugs without consuming lethal quantities of either, easing while under the influence, the anguish of consciousness. But the more you imbibe, the worse you feel when the effect wears off into the inevitable hangover, the more booze or dope you need to re-establish equilibrium.

The heartbroken jilted lover may find a remedy in the arms of another love, at the risk of landing himself into further trouble. There can be no doubt that religion, and prayer, for those who have faith, can be a curative solace, without the necessity of taking vows and entering monastery or convent.

But the agnostic can take comfort in the thought that the greatest of all healers is time; that as a starfish or a crab replaces a severed limb or claw with a new one, or broken human bones when surgically adjusted knit together, or deep flesh wounds gradually close, leaving only a scar of healthy skin, so the most painful of mental wounds will with the passing of time diminish in their hurt until at last they fade into the mists of semi-forgetfulness.

If my heart was broken, it was a slow breaking for while the shock of that Welsh letter had been great it was soon softened by my optimistic disbelief in its finality. And I had gone on hoping, sustained by a conviction that everything would come right in the end.

I had no means of knowing if the children on their return home from their first holiday with me had chattered enthusiastically about their experiences, acting, if only indirectly, as propagandists on my behalf. They must have been excited to see their mother again and she and Bertha would have showered their affection upon them. The school holidays were not yet over. If where they were living the sea was not at their front door, there was, I had gathered, a nearby stream where they could bathe, if not swim, and catch little fish. There were the ponies and other pets, including a large ill-mannered dog belonging to Bertha which they adored but I detested. Everything I was sure would be done to make their homecoming a happy one.

Yet if they hadn't talked spontaneously about their holiday with me and our various adventures, their mother must at least have been curious about the hut itself, picturing how it had been when we as lovers had first found it and joyously set about the job of making it habitable. Could she resist asking them about the garden and the stream, the bamboo shoots we had planted and nurtured so fondly, the rambler roses, the paved paths which she herself had made, the oak tree and the swing, the pool we had carved out of the rock at the sunniest side of the cove, in which we had given Ann her first dip in salt water?

Some days after their return, I'd had a brief letter from her telling me that they had arrived safely. They seemed to have enjoyed their holiday by the sea and she was glad that little

Shawn had learned to swim. He could talk about nothing else, but he and the other children were very excited because she was going to take them to a big fête and gymkhana in the grounds of the Lord of the Manor, who happened to be a real lord and the Master of the local Hunt which was a very famous one, with which the Duke of Windsor, when he was the Prince of Wales, had often ridden. (How thrilled I thought Bertha would be.) She hadn't mentioned Marie in that letter, nor had she mentioned the fat plaice.

Reading between its very scanty lines, I should have had the sense to realise that she resented—and it was a natural and forgivable resentment—my having the children to stay with me at all, that she hadn't yet budged in her decision not to live with me again.

Nor in the ensuing years, during which she and Bertha had moved their school to another mansion nearer to London, was there any indication of a change of heart. The children were allowed to stay with me for part of their summer holidays. I was granted the favour of meeting some of them for a day in London, at Christmas time, giving them an expensive lunch, taking them to shows like Peter Pan and Treasure Island, or to the Zoo and the Tower, or the South Kensington Museums. This was a mistake, for it seemed to me that I had no sooner joyously met them than I was bidding them good-bye.

There could not be another perfect August like that first one. There was one in which it rained almost every day and the winds blew spitefully from the sea without break so that it was impossible for us to visit any of the coastal coves except by hiking. There were no prawns that summer. Even in our cove the water never got really warm. There was another when a local polio outbreak delayed their coming until September, and their stay was restricted to a fortnight instead of the agreed month. I never had the whole family again at the same time.

And children grow up. Like birds from a nest they spread their wings and fly away to an independent life and only the most foolish of parents tries to hold them back. Ann with her looks and voice an undoubted asset, and her artistic temperament not, I hoped, a fatal handicap in a profession that required a rock-like stubbornness and singleness of purpose, had joined a touring repertory company.

Henrietta who had inherited her mother's passion for animals in general and horses in particular (a passion which alas! I had not shared) had finished her academic education with prizes only for "nature study" and had been at home helping her mother and Bertha. But she had confided in me that she was just longing to go to Canada and live with some friends of ours who had a ranch in Alberta. Simon and Patrick still at boarding-schools were making their own friendships. There were school holiday camps, organised Continental tours, as well as invitations to stay with their school pals in various parts of Great Britain. After that cold wet August, when even the model railway had begun to pall, I could not insist that they should always come to me, and instead left the choice to the boys themselves, although I had a suspicion that when they wrote to tell me they didn't wish to come, the decision was not uninfluenced.

Yet I'd gone on hoping, and strange though it may seem it was with a resurgence of hope that I had put my affairs in the hands of a solicitor, and filed my petition for divorce on the grounds of desertion. I was not asking for the custody of the children. It could be called an act of white blackmail. It would be a repulsive business disclosing our private life in a court of law, we who had taken that lovely poem of Shakespeare as a symbol and an inspiration of a way of living, as repulsive to my wife as it would be to me. When the action was listed for hearing and the dreadful day approached, she would I believed realise the utter stupidity of it, listen to reason, call it a day. If she didn't want to come back to our old home, and our "Under the Greenwood Tree" sort of life, then together we could find another home, perhaps even go back to Yorkshire.

II

THE MILLS of God grind slow, but not so slow as the machinery of that branch of the Judiciary of England and Wales known as the Probate, Divorce and Admiralty Division, and this was particularly so in the years following the end of Hitler's war when the number of divorce suits broke all records. But I was not in a hurry; "softly, softly catchee monkey."

I'll not pretend I was happy during those years of waiting. While I appreciated solitude I was not a hermit. Unlike Bob I was not a complete disciple of Mr. Thoreau who wanted to get away from it all. Besides Bob had the companionship of his wife. I who had known the happiness of married life was alone, and there were times when I felt very miserable indeed, yet never descending to the depths of acute melancholia.

At such times alcohol might have helped me. Perhaps I should have accepted Arthur Welsh's oft repeated invitation to have a night at the Lugger. I had a peculiar reluctance to going into any local pub. I was aware that everyone in Polruan and Fowey by this time knew that my wife and I had parted. I made no pretence with Arthur himself about it. *In vino veritas.* I didn't want to discuss my affairs in such an atmosphere, however friendly it would be, or what was worse, be in the company of people who out of "delicacy of feeling" would deliberately avoid making personal remarks, as they might do to someone recently bereaved. And to drink alone was unthinkable.

But if time is a cure for sorrow, the success of the cure depends on how you spend your time. The best thing is to lead a physically active life. I was fortunate in being able to do this. I had another book to write, but until I got near to the end, I could never sit at my typewriter for more than a couple of hours at a stretch, and that had to be in the morning, and preferably when it was raining and no urgent jobs to be done in the garden or with the boats. I economised on petrol by rarely using *Amanda* for my daily trips to Fowey. I pulled in the dinghy no matter what the weather, even into the teeth of a westerly half gale and a flood tide, and always I had my trolling line over. With this and the gardening, and sawing wood for my fires, and doing carpentering jobs I had never in my life been more physically fit.

I had to do without *Amanda* for nearly the whole of my second winter, for her leaks had steadily worsened and all my efforts to cure them had failed. She was hauled up into Toms' yard, and Jack Toms's first comment when he superficially examined her was:

"You'd do better break her up for firewood and have a new one built."

But Sam Slade's more expert verdict was less disconcerting:

"She's a very old boat, and no one's looked after her proper. Can't tell until we've got the engine out, and all her paint and tar scraped off what's got to be done, but she'll need a new keel for one thing, and extra timbers and maybe one or two planks where those lead patches are. We'll not be able to turn her into a new boat, but she's not hopeless. I've known plenty worse than her."

With the boat yard so busy and orders for new craft piling up I could not expect priority, but as the engine too had been giving me some trouble and had become very noisy even when running at half throttle, Bob took it home with him in his own Austin Seven to carry out an unhurried stripping and examination.

He was diffident in giving me his verdict when he had done this. He didn't want to depress me. He should have warned me when he had reassembled it after its immersion that it was not in very good condition. Only an early model of an Austin

Seven could have given me the service that this one had already done. No wonder it had become noisy. The main bearings and the big ends were practically gone. There was water in the sump. He had discovered a tiny hole in one of the cylinder walls and that the wall itself was only egg-shell thick. It could not be repaired. I would either have to get another engine or another block, and it would be safer to get one that had been rebored, with of course pistons to match. He knew of a firm who specialised in "old model" spares. A new block wouldn't be cheap, and it might be better to try and get hold of another reconditioned Austin Seven, but I might get stung again.

Dear Fred! I had met him several times since that day he had delivered *Amanda* and hurried off with the cheque. He had complimented me on the way I had painted her. The mast, he said, was a great improvement. He had done several other conversions since then and was still on the lookout for suitable hulls.

I liked him too much to be angry with him, but an opportunity came for me to get some of my own back. One day in stormy weather I saw a boat drifting up the creek. I pulled out in the dinghy and towed it into the cove. It was a bigger boat than *Amanda*, broad in the beam, with what is called a hard chine, virtually flat-bottomed. It had no engine, but obviously it was designed as a speed boat. Although its bottom was foul with weed and barnacles and its paintwork blistered, it was sound. I discovered through Arthur that it belonged to a man in Polruan, who had been trying to sell it for some time, as he couldn't afford to put an engine in it. He was fed up with it. It wasn't the first time it had broken away from its moorings.

I didn't want it for myself. I detested speed boats. Thinking of Fred, however, I offered the man five pounds for it, an offer which to my surprise he promptly accepted. It was certainly worth ten pounds for its timber alone.

I did not rush things with Fred. Again, "softly, softly, catchee monkey." I met him in Fowey one day—it was during the winter that *Amanda* was laid up—and invited him to come over and have a cup of tea with me. He saw the boat; I could tell by his assumed lack of interest in it that he was interested. He was biting. It was not until we'd had tea and I'd shown him round the garden that he mentioned the boat and asked me what I was going to do with it. I was at least partly honest in telling him that I hadn't quite made up my mind, that I'd bought it as a spec., that I might have an engine put in it and perhaps sell it. We walked down to the cove again and this time he did have a closer look at it, and all the time I was saying to myself "how much did you pay for the hull of *Amanda*, darling Fred, and how much for the engine, and how much did you make me pay for it?"

Perhaps he sensed that our roles now were reversed, that he was the buyer, I the seller. He hadn't the nerve, it wouldn't be buyer-seller etiquette, to ask me how much I had paid for it. But in the end he did say with a well-feigned air of not being too keen that he wouldn't mind buying it at a reasonable price. What did I want for it?"

I said, and I should have blushed:

"She's worth at least fifty. I'll take half of that to a friend."

He laughed.

"I can't afford twenty-five. It's going to need a pretty big engine and it might be a long time before I get hold of a suitable one. She's not worth all that to me."

"*It is naught, it is naught, saith the buyer, but when he is gone his way then he boasteth.*"

I was silent. Fred was silent too while he was looking sideways at the boat. And then he said:

"I'll give you twenty; that's my absolute limit."

Dear Fred! He should have made a fortune, and lived a longer life. Some months later I happened to recognise that boat tied up to the Albert Quay. She had been partly decked and furnished with a glazed wheelhouse, and of course an engine. She was beautifully painted, and she had been given a name, printed in gilt on her transom. Discreet inquiries revealed that she now belonged to a retired civil servant, that her engine was converted from a Fordson tractor (I'd seen one advertised for twenty pounds) and that the price the owner had paid to Fred was two hundred and fifty!

III

I MIGHT have been lonely during the years of waiting, I was never bored. There were very few days, even in the winter, when I could not fish, if not at sea then in the harbour or up-river. I was not particularly fond of fish, no matter how they were cooked, but I had plenty of friends in Fowey and Pol-ruan to whom I could give them, and occasionally if I happened to make a big catch I'd sell them to Percy Varco, who owned the Fowey fishmonger's shop, a great friend of mine, who did a bit of fishing himself with net and long line. He had once been a professional footballer, playing for Aston Villa for many seasons.

My cat, however, was the chief recipient of my fish, and very often the justification for a trip when my conscience might have said no. He was given to me by a friend of Wilfred's. I called him Choo-i, after the castaway tabby we'd had in our old days in the hut, although he was a neutered male. I'd been reluctant at first to have him for this reason, for while my admiration for all members of his tribe from tigers, leopards, pumas, cheetahs, cervals, lynxs, down to domestic kittens, was life-long, I had an antipathy towards the typical sophisticated, over-fed, over-weight, lethargic, cushion-loving city and suburban sexless Tom. Choo-i, although a eunuch, had not surrendered his feline jungle heritage. He was black, with one white patch on his chest and green eyes that were like jewels.

"A cat offers no angles to the Wind." He had a superb and lean body, with a short-haired, smooth sleek coat so that you could see the rippling of his muscles under it; his belly distended only to the size of the meal he had taken. Sitting on his haunches in front of my fire on a winter's night, or curled up on the rug asleep, with his tail smoothly bent to the shape of his torso, he might have been posing for a drawing or sculpture, aware of his own exciting beauty.

Yet, as all cats should be, he was a hunter. I'd watch him from the window of the big room, where I had my work-table, standing close to a clump of thick grass by the side of the path, peering at the grass, absolutely static but for a slight trembling at the tip of his outstretched tail. Suddenly this trembling would increase, and he would rise on his hind legs, like a squirrel. And then he would pounce, leaping perhaps a yard into the air and then down, into the grass. There would be a scuffling. Then leisurely he would move out of the grass on to the path and walk up to the little lawn opposite the big room door and veranda, the mouse usually still alive in his mouth, and deposit it on the lawn. If he was hungry and it was alive he would give it the *coup de gráce*, and start eating it head first, leaving only the entrails. If he was in a sporting mood he would let it go, deliberately look the other way, then catch it again, toss it up in the air and leap after it. I objected to this of course. I'd rush out and kill the mouse myself. He would show no resentment except to give me a rather puzzled look. His manners always were perfect.

Choo-i had an amazing intelligence. I talked to him as I would do to a human being and I was certain that he understood. There was a robin who always appeared whenever I started digging in the garden, and it was so tame that it would take a worm out of my hand. I told Choo-i that there would be hell to pay if ever he touched that robin, and as though the robin understood too it would often perch within easy range of Choo-i's claws, and Choo-i would not even glance at it. He was indeed a good companion especially when my loneliness did get me down, those still dark winter evenings when the only sound would be the hooting of an owl and the babbling of the stream in which sometimes I could imagine

I heard the voices of my children, saying over and over again,
"Daddy, Daddy, Daddy." Then Choo-i would leap on to my
lap, make himself comfortable, and stare at me with his green
eyes, and purr, as much as to say:

"Cheer up, old cock. We're not dead yet!"

Such moods were rare, however, and I had myself to blame
for them, for I had a standing invitation to go to Waldon's
Pond and see Bob and Joyce whenever I felt like company.
It was only a short bus ride to St. Blazey and then a half-mile
walk. If I didn't feel like staying the night Bob would bring
me back to Fowey and my dinghy in his Austin Seven.

His place was aptly named. His cottage had been the offices
of the china clay pit owners. The pit itself, long ago worked
out, was flooded to make a deep circular pond at least two
acres in size. The debris from the pit, piled irregularly along
its perimeter, was grown over with alder, sallow, and furze.
Bob had cleared some of this to give vistas of the pond, and
had the trees been maple and pines Thoreau himself could
have imagined he was home.

The buildings, there were two of them with a common wall,
were of huge rough-hewn granite blocks. One of them was single
story with two largish, ceilingless, flag-floored rooms. The other
was double-storied, making a garage for the Austin Seven at
ground level, and a bedroom reached by an outside staircase
above. The roofs were of thick slate slabs.

They had made a wonderful job of reconstruction, for which
they'd had no professional help. They'd put in new windows,
doors, fireplaces. Luckily they had piped water, and they
were near enough to a grid transformer for electricity. Bob
had done the installation himself, and his cooking stove, water
heater, stainless steel sink, all beautifully streamlined, made me
very envious.

He was a perfectionist in all that he did. When I made a
cupboard or a bookcase, I would slam the planks together,
filling the joints with putty if they did not fit accurately.
Paint would hide all such blemishes. Bob would dovetail his

216

joints, fit them so that there wouldn't be a hair's breadth between them. It was the same with his engineering. But such scrupulous attention to detail took time, which would have made him an unprofitable employee at a garage where, if skill and thoroughness were the prime consideration, he might have been earning twice the money he was getting from reading meters.

Would he as a perfectionist ever find his *métier* on the stage? I never ceased to badger him about this, but to no avail. He knew what he wanted and he'd got it, or would have it when he could throw and bake what would be to him at least a satisfactory piece of pottery; and by that he didn't mean an ash-tray or a little vase with a motto or "A Present from Fowey" or "Waldon's Pond" inscribed upon it, but something that had real beauty in shape and colour.

In one of the ground level rooms he was building a big professional kiln of special firebricks. As this would take a long time he had installed a small kiln, electrically fired. Here too, he had his potter's wheel, which he had made himself: a box of clay (not the ubiquitous china clay of the district), with a wet sack over it to keep it moist: a chemical balance to weigh out the various ingredients used for making glazes: a rack of tools, scores of bottles and jars on shelves: everything—in contrast to my own workshop and writing-table—neat and tidy.

He would not, however, show me any of the products of his kiln. I must wait until he had made something he was not ashamed of.

He and Joyce were my closest and dearest friends. But there was Arthur Welsh who rarely missed a week without calling on me; garrulous old Sharkie who'd come up the creek every low spring tide to dig bait. I was on the friendliest terms with the manager, the foremen and artisans of the Brazen Island Shipyard, where they were now building an 800-ton steel coaster. It was always a joy to me, apart from watching the repairing of *Amanda*, to wander round Toms's yard.

There never was a friendlier people than the Cornish,

provided you didn't put on airs with them, or pretend you were anything but what you were. The china clay stevedores, the captains and crews of the dredger and tugs, the pilots, the boatmen, the shipping agents, the jovial harbour master, Captain Collins, who tried to convert me into becoming a "Jehovah's Witness," the tradespeople of Polruan and Fowey—I was friends with them all. Even those who were not natives— and there were many of these—seemed to be infected by this atmosphere of geniality. Was it the Cornish sun, the sea air, that performed this miracle?

There was the ever-friendly Wilfred, and the Galant's Club, with its occasional Saturday night hops to the music of radio or gramophone. Fond though I was of dancing I could not bring myself to go to them. For dancing I had to be in the right mood, a mood that was customarily induced by at least a little alcohol. The club was "dry" and there was my diffidence about pubs. A student of Freud might have given a different interpretation to this reluctance of mine to join in the dance, but the professor himself could not have guessed its ultimate effect on my fortunes.

There was a cinema in Fowey where occasionally there were excellent films, no worse for being dated ones like Fred Astaire's gorgeous *Easter Parade*. Television had not as yet reached the West of England. I had an elderly but good battery-operated radio, and a more elderly but excellent wind-up cabinet gramophone. Except that I did not like jazz and detested crooning, I was not too choosy about my music. I could listen with different emotions yet as happily to the music of Irving Berlin, Jerome Kern, Rogers and Hammerstein, as I could to that of Beethoven, Bach, Chopin; to *Oklahoma* and *Annie Get Your Gun* as to Beethoven's "Pastoral Symphony" or Chopin's "Prelude in A Flat Major."

I had a good selection of dance records, some that were "vocal" with lyrics of the most sickening sentimentality. This did not distress me so long as the rhythm was right, fox-trot, quickstep, waltz or tango. Often I would dance by myself or pick up Choo-i and dance with him in my arms. To the music of *Swan Lake* I'd try ballet movement, with Choo-i eyeing me superciliously from the fireside rug, and I tried to teach myself tap dancing but without success. How I envied the agility, the perfect artistry of Fred Astaire.

I had books to read and reread.

I never tired of the beauty of the creek, whether the tide was full or low, its water rough or calm; its banks summer green or ablaze with the reds and golden yellows of autumn, or its trees naked to the winter winds or bursting with the darling buds of May.

I was never free of a yearning for the companionship of my family, but time was healing the wound. It is not true that absence makes the heart grow fonder, and I had the consolation that whatever happened at least some of the children would spend a part of their summer holiday with me.

IV

ONCE you have committed yourself to an action for divorce you are advised by your solicitor that from henceforth you must not in any circumstances communicate directly with the person you once addressed as "darling," "sweetheart," "beloved," "precious one," who is now referred to as your spouse. Whatever you have to say must be written to your own solicitor, who unless he thinks you are saying something that may prejudice your case, will have a copy made, and send a carbon copy of this letter to your spouse's solicitor, who will duplicate the process.

This calls for the expenditure of your solicitor's and his typist's valuable time and an appropriate charge is made for it when you get your final bill.

It was summer again, late June, and now eleven years since we had parted. I'd had a letter from my solicitor to say that it had been agreed that Shawn and Henrietta were to come to me for the usual four weeks in August, and that as Henrietta was of a responsible age there would be no insistence on my having a housekeeper for the period. The letter also informed me that as there was a still heavy list of cases to be heard there was little chance of mine coming on in the present term, but there was a strong probability that it would do so next term, and be heard before Christmas.

At the beginning of July I was surprised to receive a letter in my wife's (or rather spouse's) own hand-writing. I was shaking when I opened it, wondering again if the miracle had happened. It hadn't, but it was most friendly in its tone.

Henrietta, it said, had a definite invitation to stay for at least a year with our friends who owned a ranch in Alberta. It was just the sort of life she would love, and she was terribly excited about it. Our friends had offered to pay for her passage, and the long railway journey, but the snag was that it seemed impossible to get a berth in any ship sailing to Canada or the U.S.A. Every berth was booked for months ahead. She had tried all the big passenger ship companies and agents. She wasn't going to risk going by air. I had a lot of friends connected with the shipping world. Could I persuade any of them to use their influence in getting a berth? It would be necessary, of course, for me to give my formal permission for her to leave the country, and this would have to be done through our solicitors. And if she did get a berth it would mean that Shawn would have to come on his own for the summer holiday, but she was sure that Marie would come instead. Shawn was going to miss Henrietta very much for he adored her. But he did like Marie.

She knew she was breaking the rules in writing to me direct, but she was only thinking of Henrietta's happiness.

Apart from the reference to "our solicitors" no one reading that letter could have imagined that we were husband and wife with a suit for divorce impending.

I had collected it at the Fowey post office and gone into the nearby Galant's Club, as usual deserted early in the morning, to open it. My feelings were mixed. It was a blow that Henrietta might not be coming to me as arranged. She was a darling, so generous, full of fun, as devoted to Shawn as he was to her. And I knew that it was going to hurt her mother to let her go, a deep sacrifice. But I could have no doubt about my own course of action.

To hell with the lawyers and their silly, but to them profitable professional etiquette! I must do my best to do what was asked of me.

Truth is often stranger than fiction. How often had I found this to be so in my career as a professional writer. Soon after we had first moved into our hut a tramp steamer had been brought into the creek to be laid up, this being during the

great depression which had followed the end of the Kaiser's
war. To my dismay, for we were then trying to live incognito,
I recognised the officer in charge of this ship as a native of my
own Yorkshire village. We had been schoolmates, or rather
school enemies. With greater dismay I recognised a lady who
was also on the ship and clearly his wife as the daughter of a
village tradesman to whom I was unfortunately in debt.

For several weeks we did our best to avoid them. I even grew
a beard as disguise. In the end the strain was too much for me.
I went aboard the ship. There was mutual recognition. I
found my boyhood enemy completely mellowed and friendly,
delighted to meet someone from " t'awd spot," and his wife was
equally friendly, both of them promising to keep mum in their
letters home. It was indeed a sad day for us when nearly a year
later the ship was sold to the Greeks, and sailed with our friends
on board for Falmouth and dry dock, and to be handed over to
her new owners. . . .

Close to the harbour office on the Albert Quay were the
offices of Toyne and Carter, the old established shipping agents.
We had been friendly with Jack Toyne, one of the partners, in
the old days. He had been a great admirer of my wife. He was
very tall, lanky, grey-haired, with a deeply-lined intellectual
face, more like a university don than a businessman. He
affected a gloomy misanthropy, and had a sardonic sense of
humour. He had ragged me about my present circumstances,
the fact that our marriage had foundered. He said that the fault
must be mine. That my wife was far too good for me. But
underneath this ragging I was aware of a sympathetic
understanding.

I found him in his office, seated at his desk, studying,
through horn-rimmed reading glasses, a copy of *Lloyd's List*
and *Shipping Gazette*. He removed his glasses and gave me a
sardonic smile:

"Sit down," he said. "What's wrong? You look worried.
Has she decided to forgive all and come back to you?"

I told him that I was trying to get a steamship berth for

Henrietta to go to Canada, tourist, second class, even first (I would pay the difference myself), even steerage. The walls of his office were decorated with posters of all the big and intermediate British and foreign passenger ship companies.

He said brusquely:

"There's not a hope in hell, for three months at least. Even if your daughter was a film star. Have you forgotten we're only starting to recover from the war, with more than half the world's shipping sunk?"

"What about cargo ships, Jack? They do take passengers occasionally, don't they?"

"They do, but not a young girl like your daughter, pretty too, if she's anything like her mother." He was silent for a moment and then he said:

"We've got a Whitby ship up at the jetties at present, loading for Montreal, the *Glaisdale*. Have you seen her? She's at Number 8 jetty. Whitby's your own port, isn't it?"

My heart was thumping.

No. 8 was the remotest of the clay loading jetties. I hadn't been up-river for several days, and ships arriving often came in and berthed during the night. If I had seen one of that name, with Whitby painted on her stern as her port of registry, I would have called on her in the hope of meeting someone I knew.

"Who's her skipper? Does he come from Whitby?"

"No, he's a Cardiff man. Captain Tom Grainger. Doesn't sound like a Taffy, does it?"

Grainger . . . Grainger . . . Grainger . . . The name suddenly clicked. There had been Graingers in my own village when I was a boy. There had been a Captain Jim, with at least two sons, one of them called Tom, who had attended the village school and I remembered that Captain Jim had emigrated with his family to Cardiff before his boys had left school. It was natural that they would have followed his profession.

I tried to keep calm.

"When's she sailing?"

"Now don't get excited. I don't think there's an earthly chance of fixing things up with her, but it's worth trying. I think she'll be away to-morrow night."

I was already on the move. I had come over in *Amanda*, since her overhaul in perfect trim. I went at full speed up-river. At the fourth jetty the river turns abruptly to the left, and there were jetties No. 5, 6, 7, and 8, with *Glaisdale* tied to No. 8, her bow pointing down river. She was a typical pre-war British tramp, about six thousand tons, one of the few survivors of mine, U-boat and air attack.

Glaisdale was the name of a moorland village some miles inland from Whitby, and I was trying to think which of the several shipping companies whose headquarters were at Whitby (despite that Whitby's harbour was too small for anything but fishing vessels and coasters), named their ships after local places. I was soon to know.

I made fast to the bottom of the *Glaisdale's* companion ladder, climbed aboard. Loading was in progress, and the decks were white with clay dust. I asked a young sailor if the captain was on board and if so would he direct me to his cabin. The man answered with a familiar Yorkshire accent.

"Aye, I reckon he is. Up yon ladder, then straight ahead, and if he's not in his cabin he's maybe in t' saloon."

I knocked at the door of the cabin, from which there came the noise of a typewriter. A voice said "Come in." I opened the door and saw seated at a table, with a typewriter in front of him, a middle-aged man with greying hair, a roundish pleasant clean-shaven face, whom I would have spotted anywhere as a seafarer.

"Captain Grainger?" I said.

He was staring hard at me.

"Aye; that's me. Who are you? There's something familiar about your face."

"There's something familiar about yours too. Didn't you once live at Robin Hood's Bay? Aren't you one of Captain Jim Grainger's sons?"

He rose from the table, reached out his hand:

"By gum! I know you. I thought there was something familiar about your face. Well, by gum . . . Sit down. Have a drink. Of course I'm Tom Grainger. Dad's living at Bay now. He's over eighty, but still going strong. Well, I *am* pleased to see you. What'll you have?"

Under ordinary circumstances I could happily have gone on yarning with Captain Tom for hours. But, talking and listening to each other about the village we knew and loved and its folk, some long since dead and gone, some like Tom's own father still going strong, I was wondering how I could decently bring the subject round to my present urgent problem. I sipped warily at the generous tot of whisky he had poured out for me, noting that his own tot was a token one only. He had given me a cigar that Winston himself would not have turned up his nose at. He was kindness itself. If he had to say no to my proposition, I knew he would do it with reluctance.

I got a lead in at last by asking him innocently when he was sailing and what his destination would be, and when he said to-morrow evening, and it was Montreal, I made the leap.

He listened in silence, and I could tell he was bothered. When I had done he was still silent for a while. Then he said:

"Well, you're asking something and no mistake. A young lass like that in a tramp steamer. Of course there's accommodation. There's the pilot's cabin, always ready in case the weather's too rough for the pilot to get back into his boat. That couldn't happen on this voyage. I couldn't take her without the owners agreeing, or I'd get into trouble. But, by gum, Leo, I'd like to help you."

Again he was silent. Then he said:

"I won't say yes and I won't say no. I'll tell you what I'll do. How did you get here, walking or in a boat?"

"In my old motor boat. She's tied to your ladder."

"Then let's get down to the agents. I've got to ring up the owners in any case to-day. Do you know Mr. Headlam, boss of the company? He lives in a big house near Whitby. A very

decent chap. I'll put it to him but don't bank on it. Do you
think your lass will have all her papers ready? There's not
much time. Finish your drink and come on."

I had the sense not to touch any more of that whisky. I'd
need to keep my wits about me. It was going to be a feather in
my cap if this business came off. It would be a proof that a
husband and father could be of use. It might indeed be the
beginning of the end.

Jack Toyne put one of the office telephones at the captain's
disposal in a private room. Jack, who had some other business
to attend to, left me to wait in his own office. It seemed hours
before the door opened, and the captain came in, and he was
beaming.

"We're in luck," he said. "He hummed and hawed about it
at first—said he'd never heard of such a proposition. I told
him who you were and that you really came from Bay and that
you knew my dad. In the end he said he'd leave it to me. And
there we are. I've got to be straight with you. She's got to be
on board before sailing time. And there'll be a charge to the
company of five quid to cover the cost of her food. The point
is can you get her here in time. We can't hold up sailing even
for five minutes."

I was incapable of speech. I could only grasp Tom's hand.
Then Jack came in.

"What's happened?" he asked.

The captain answered, "It's O.K., Mr. Toyne, so far as the
company's concerned, if the lass can get here in time. We
should be sailing at six."

Jack turned to me.

"Is your dear wife on the telephone? Letters will be no good.
Where is she living now?"

I told him. And that she was on the telephone, but I just
knew that I would not have the courage to speak to her myself,
to hear her voice.

"Jack," I said, "will you do it for me? She knows you. You
know what to say. Frankly, I funk it."

I thought that Tom was looking a little embarrassed.

"Look," he said, "I'll get out of the way. I've got a bit of shopping to do. I'll be back say in twenty minutes."

He went, and then Jack said, only half ironically:

"You're a queer man, not wanting to talk to your own wife, that is if you *do* want her back, but I suppose you know your own business best. Shall I do it from here or on the other phone?"

"I'd rather you did it in private."

He grinned. "I trust you realise that you're using up the time of an extremely busy man. Give me the number. Shall I give her your love, or not?"

I wished while I waited that I had finished that tot of whisky. I felt ashamed of my cowardice. Or was I jealous that another man should be talking as an accepted friend to my own wife?

He came back.

"Did you get her, Jack?"

"Yes. But I wouldn't have recognised her voice. And there was a hell of a racket going on as though she was speaking from a nursery full of kids. She seemed a bit shocked but very pleased. It was going to be an awful rush, but she'd do her utmost to get Henrietta on to the Cornish Riviera to-morrow, and would you write off to-day to your solicitor, to let her solicitor know you gave permission. I told her she'd have to get Henrietta vaccinated."

"Did you," I asked, "give her my love?"

"I did, but I couldn't quite make out what she said, there was too much noise. And now be off with you and let a busy man get on with his work. You're a bloody nuisance!"

227

V

THE MAIN railway line, once known as the Great Western, which runs from London's Paddington to Penzance by way of Reading, Taunton, Exeter, Plymouth and Truro, has numerous offshoots, one of which is at Lostwithiel, at the tidal head of the River Fowey, six miles from Fowey itself. Here is a single track line skirting the picturesque river bank, passing the little village of Golant and finally passing by the jetties into Fowey Station.

The most famous of the main line trains, the Cornish Riviera, which leaves Paddington at 10.30 a.m. does not stop at Lostwithiel. It goes on west another six miles to Par, from which another branch line runs north to Newquay. Passengers for Fowey get out at Par and complete their journey either by bus or taxi. Henrietta, if all had gone well, was due to arrive at Par at a quarter to four. Even the bus would land her at Fowey within another twenty minutes, and with the *Glaisdale* due to cast off at six, there should have been ample time to embark.

At a quarter-past four the next afternoon I was waiting at the slipway landing of the Fowey-Bodinnick car ferry, close to Fowey Railway Station, in a state of great anxiety. The loading of the *Glaisdale* had been completed before schedule. Another ship was waiting to occupy her berth. She would be casting off at half-past four. This information had been brought to me by Toyne & Carter's boatman at three o'clock, just as I was setting out for Fowey, and it was confirmed by Jack himself when I called at the office.

I had intended to meet Henrietta in a taxi. Jack, however,

had insisted that he should meet her in his own car, which was a powerful one. It would be safer for me to stand by at the landing place. Unless the train was late, he would be there at four.

From where I waited I could not see the up-river jetties. They were round the bend. But already I had seen the two Fowey tugs steam past at what in my anxiety seemed to be at an unusually great speed and disappear round the bend. They would now be closing in on the ship, preparing to take on their lines. That operation I reckoned would take about ten minutes. Another five and the mooring lines of the ship would be cast off, and slowly she would be eased away from the berth. With one tug ahead to do the actual towing, and the other astern as a check on speed and course, the *Glaisdale* would be under way for the harbour and the open sea.

I had no watch. Close to the landing place was the shop of J. Bennett and Sons, grocers and ship chandlers with a clock which, the genial John Bennett assured me, kept Greenwich time. I had explained to him why I was so anxious. At a quarter-past four at my urgent request he had telephoned to Par station. The line was engaged. At twenty past he had tried again, and was able to tell me that the train, half an hour late, was just steaming in.

I paced up and down between the landing place where *Amanda*, with her engine in neutral and ticking over, was made fast, and the shop with its clock, scarcely daring to look up-river, praying that every car I heard coming down the road would be Jack's. My heart came into my mouth when from up-river came the deep blast of a steamer's horn.

The clock moved to half-past, to five-and-twenty to five, and still no Jack. What had happened? Driving only tolerably fast he should have been here in under fifteen minutes. I was tortured by the gloomiest thoughts. Had Henrietta been unable to get a seat on the train? It was holiday time of course. Had she got out at Plymouth by mistake, thinking she must change to the one that stopped at Lostwithiel for the Fowey connexion?

Most terrible thought of all, had Jack in his urgency driven too fast and crashed?

The leading tug had appeared at the corner of the bend, moving at right angles to the main fairway. Then came the foremast of the *Glaisdale*, her funnel and superstructure and aftermast, her hull temporarily hidden by the loading machinery of Jetty No. 5. Slowly she cleared to become wholly visible, and the leading tug began to swing her round the bend, the second tug towing at her stern. She slewed round to her course. In another five minutes she would be nearly opposite to where I was waiting. Another quarter of an hour and she would be at the harbour mouth.

I heard the sound of another car approaching. There was a toot as it drew up and stopped. It was Jack, and it was Henrietta. I rushed to it. Jack was out first and was striding round to the boot. I helped Henrietta out, hugged her and she hugged me back and kissed me on the cheek.

"Are we too late, Daddy?" she asked.

"No, darling, you'll get on board somehow."

"Not if you don't look lively," shouted Jack. He was lifting a cabin trunk out of the boot. "Is your boat here?"

The *Glaisdale* was now half-way down the straight. The after tug had cast off having fulfilled her purpose. I helped Jack carry the trunk into *Amanda*. Henrietta, carrying a rucksack and a small parcel, got in, and I got in too, but Jack stayed.

"I warned the captain that we might be a bit late," he said, "but I hadn't reckoned on a blasted traffic jam. He'll have left the companion ladder down. It'll be on her port side. And don't you dare to ask me to do any more emigrations for you. Good luck, Henrietta. Give my regards to Captain Grainger. Don't you go vamping him."

"Jack, you're a saint!" I shouted, as he cast off our painter.

"Thank you, thank you!" shouted Henrietta.

I put the engine ahead and opened the throttle. I was too tense now to speak. The tug was less than a hundred yards

away. I dared to cross her bows, which brought *Amanda* onto
the port side of the *Glaisdale*. The captain of the tug waved to
us and then as we drew near the ship I recognised Tom on the
bridge (with the pilot at his side) and he waved too and pointed
to the companion ladder, at the foot of which stood two sailors
waiting for us. I made a circuit so as to approach the ladder
from the stern, and I think then that the tug must have slowed
down a little for I made the ladder without difficulty. One of
the sailors grasped the painter and made it fast. I stopped my
own engine. We were being towed. The trunk was on the
foredeck. The sailors took charge of it, and Henrietta prepared
to get out. But before she did she gave me another hug and a
kiss, and handed me the small parcel she had been carrying.

"It's a present from Mummy," she said.

She got out, climbed the ladder. Leaning over the bridge
rails, Captain Tom waved to me, and at the top of the ladder
Henrietta gave me a last wave. I saw that she was having a hard
job to keep back her tears. The sailor cast off my painter.
With my engine dead, I dropped astern along the ship's side,
into her wake. She was not yet using her own power. I could
have started again and escorted her down the harbour. But
there was no point in prolonging the sadness of farewell. I
looked at the parcel that Henrietta had given me. I opened it.
It contained a pullover, rust red, my favourite colour, beautifully knitted in the diamond and cable pattern of the Yorkshire
fishermen, a pattern my wife had learned from my own fishermen
friends.

There was no letter with it. If there had been, I could not
have read it then; my eyes were full of tears.

VI

My hopes that the successful embarkation of Henrietta might have a highly favourable domestic consequence, that the unexpected gift of the lovely pullover was itself symbolic of a change of heart, were soon dashed.

I had sent a telegram to my wife to say that Henrietta was safely on board the ship. With malicious satisfaction at depriving our solicitors of still more money to go on their bill, I had followed the telegram with a long letter, in which I had given details of the get-away; the splendid part our old friend Jack Toyne had played in the operation. I told her that although the *Glaisdale* was just a tramp steamer, the accommodation would be much better than what she would get, even first class on any passenger liner, with a cabin to herself. The captain, a family man, was a grand fellow, and she would be well looked after on the voyage which should be a calm weather one.

I told her how thrilled I had been with her gift. And I dared to say how nice it was to be writing to her direct. What a pity we couldn't go on doing this. How nice it would be if she would come with Shawn in August and put an end to all this miserable business of solicitors and divorce.

Her answer to that letter was brief. She thanked me for what I had done, and she was writing to Jack Toyne to thank him too. She was glad that I liked the pullover. Shawn, who was very sad at losing Henrietta, was looking forward to his stay with me. She trusted that Marie would be able to come and keep house for me again.

A few days later, however, I received a letter from my own solicitor. It said that he had been informed by my wife's solicitor (I was glad he didn't say spouse's) that she had decided to withdraw her defence of the action. This meant that it would be transferred to the undefended list and probably lead to an earlier hearing in the Michaelmas term. The letter concluded with a reminder that in no circumstances must I communicate with my wife direct. Evidently he had smelt a rat.

That letter gave me little satisfaction. Her defence I believed was bluff, as my own petition had been. While it was a relief to learn that there would be no fight, I didn't see that there was any point in obtaining a divorce. It would save a lot of money, and deprive our respected solicitors of further spoils if I withdrew the petition myself.

But the holidays were drawing near. It looked as though we might have another perfect summer. And my darling Shawn was coming. I had gone on doing improvements to the house. The National Electric Grid had been extended to Polruan with the high tension cables running near enough for a con-nexion from a transformer to the house. Bob had done the wiring for me, with lighting and power points in every room. The second-hand bottle gas cooker had been replaced with a brand new electric one. I had bought a second-hand vacuum cleaner, and the bathroom cylinder had been fitted with an immersion heater, so I need only use the boiler stove in cold weather. Everything now was completely Mod. Con. The flower beds were looking at their best. The vegetable garden, the fruit trees all flourishing. I had a strawberry bed full of luscious fruit, and ripening tomatoes.

If only I could persuade my wife to spend one day here with Shawn, I was sure she would never want to go back to her mansion, full of screaming infants.

I had written to Marie. To my dismay she informed me that she had already arranged to spend the holidays with some Scottish friends. I wrote to Ann, half hoping that she had left her touring repertory company, and that she might come. It was nearly the end of July when I got her answer. She was in the West Riding of Yorkshire, still with the company (which was playing to very poor houses because of the weather, she thought), but the tour was going to continue till September.

I was in a jam. I could look after Shawn on my own, but it would be difficult to do all the meals, and keep the place tolerably clean and tidy. He was now an expert swimmer. He had inherited my interest in marine zoology. He was mad on fishing. But he was going to hanker after the companionship of Henrietta, the love and petting of his mother. Marie would have compensated for this. I wondered if after all it would be best for him to put off his visit.

It was the Saturday afternoon before Bank Holiday, the weather gloriously fine, Fowey and the harbour packed with happy holidaymakers. I'd gone over to get my mail and to do my shopping. Passing the Town Hall, abutting the Town Quay, I had seen a hand-printed placard announcing that a touring repertory company was giving a performance of *Love on the Dole* that evening at 8.0 p.m. I had seen the original production of *Love on the Dole* with Wendy Hiller playing the part of Sally Hardcastle. I thought of Ann and her "poor houses" and I felt that I owed this enterprise my support. The highest price on the placard was four shillings for a front seat. The doors, however, were shut, and I decided I could safely risk not booking.

I sat at my table in the big room when I got back from Fowey, feeling very dejected. The tide was up, the creek smooth and there was a traffic of pleasure boats moving up and down, most of them with children and adults on board, all so happy in the sunshine. But the cove itself, although I had never put any notice up to indicate that it was private, was deserted. I was thinking of that first glorious summer holiday, seeing my own children playing there, swimming, splashing each other, yelling with delight, of how high my hopes had been then of a reconciliation.

Now it looked as though it would never happen. It was defeat and I had better admit it. Should I write to my wife and tell her that as Marie could not come we had better put

Shawn's visit off until next summer? Wouldn't it be more sensible still if I gave up the fight, cut my losses, wrote to my solicitors telling them to withdraw the petition, sold the boats and my bits of furniture and packed up from Cornwall with its poignant memories for ever?

If I could get a berth for Henrietta on a cargo ship so easily and so cheaply, might I not do the same for myself and go awandering round the world? There were so many countries and places I would like to see: Greece and its antiquities: the Far East, Japan, if not China: Australia's Great Barrier Reef: America's National Parks and the Painted Desert: the islands of the South Seas. In a sailing boat not much bigger than *Amanda* and with cabin accommodation I might emulate the voyages of Captain Slocum, and Doctor Pye in his *Moonraker*.

What was the good of making a home if there was no one save my darling Choo-i to share it except for a few weeks in the summer?

I was not feeling any happier when I set off for Fowey again that evening. The prospect of sitting on a hard wood chair for a couple of hours watching a play I had already seen performed by famous artists was not inviting. I had on one occasion, and from similar altruistic motives gone to a repertory performance in the Town Hall of a Tennessee Williams play. It had been so bad, not the play but the players, that I had walked out at the first interval. It was not however given by the same company.

I had, anyway, made myself presentable for this occasion. I'd shaved, put on a clean shirt, even a tie; my best flannel bags, socks and shoes instead of my usual rubber deck boots, and also my new rust colour pullover. It had a V-neck, and my tie, a plain mustard yellow, harmonised with this very nicely. I'd recently had my hair cut. It was a respectable length and neatly combed. While there were streaks of grey in it, it was still predominantly brown. I was favoured with the sort of skin that takes on a deep tan in summer. Thus attired and groomed no one was going to mistake me for a tramp, or, it is true, a member of the Athenæum Club on holiday.

There were two entrances into the Town Hall, which was a very ancient building. The main one was reached by two flights of granite steps. There was, significantly, no queue waiting on the steps when I arrived just before eight o'clock. At the entrance door stood a frail, sad-looking elderly lady in a black dress, who however managed a wan smile when I asked for a front seat.

I entered and halted. Although the sun was still shining outside, the window blinds were down and the electric lights were on. There were not, I saw at first glance, more than half a dozen people in the room. The only occupants of the front seats were an elderly clergyman and a lady who presumably was his wife. Midway were two more elderly ladies, and there were two youths in the shilling seats. There was, compared with the crowded street I had just left, a deadly silence. Then there appeared from a door to the right of the stage a girl with a mass of golden hair, that was slightly unkempt. She was dressed in a pretty summer frock. In her hand was a sheaf of papers. She hurried up the aisle towards me and smiled, a very pleasant smile, which however I took to express no more than pleasure that the audience had increased by one.

She took my ticket.

"Anywhere in the first four rows," she said. Her voice was velvet and she didn't say "Sir." "Programme?"

I paid sixpence for a single flimsy sheet of hand-duplicated paper and I walked down and took my seat three rows back from the clergyman and his wife. Again there was silence in the hall, but through the tail of my eye, I observed that the girl was in sight, standing near the entrance, waiting, I supposed, for another customer. I dared to look round so that I could see her better. She was attractive, very attractive. I liked her hair. She had nice eyes and nose. She was short with a good figure. But it was her smile that had got me. It had been so warm and friendly. Although she was not wearing theatrical make-up,

I guessed that she was an actress. In such an outfit as this, members of the company shared in its chores, programme selling being one of them.

I looked at the programme. It was so badly duplicated that it was quite indecipherable beyond the boldly printed title of the play itself.

There was no visible clock in the hall. The time must have advanced beyond the specified eight, and still there were no more customers. If there had been, perhaps some of them at least might have had the courage to begin an ironic clapping for the curtain to go up. Shortly the girl walked down the aisle again and disappeared through the side door. I saw the clergyman whispering to his wife. I wouldn't have been very surprised if he had stood up and announced the opening hymn, for the atmosphere, the deadly silence, was that of a church, more so indeed when it was broken by the chimes of the nearby parish church, striking quarter past eight.

And then at last the stage curtain was drawn, but only to reveal a youngish, pale-faced man in a serge suit. There was no need for him to hold up his hand for silence. He made a speech. He was the manager of the company. Very regretfully he had to announce that he had decided that there would be no performance, as he did not feel that his company could do justice to such a fine play as *Love on the Dole* before an audience which although select was so small. All money of course would be refunded at the door.

I had never in my gayest days had the courage to call at a stage door in the hope of meeting a lady who had impressed me with her charm or beauty during the performance. Even now it was chiefly because I felt an almost paternal sympathy with these travelling thespians, because my daughter Ann might have been one of them, that having embarrassingly got my money back I walked round to the back entrance of the hall in a parallel street. I reached it just as the girl with the golden hair was coming out. Her smile now was one of recognition.

"Hallo," I said. "We meet again. Do you mind if I talk to you?"

This time the smile warmed to a chuckle.

"Of course not. Are you furious about the play and the programme I sold you? I hope you got your money back for that?"

I hadn't. I'd still got it in my hand.

"I was disappointed about the play," I said. "But it must have been more disappointing for the company, looking at all those empty seats. But if Wendy Hiller herself had been in the cast, she wouldn't have got a full house on a fine summer evening like this. I guess your programme selling was only one of a repertory company's chores. You're an actress, aren't you?"

Her answer was modest, but not over reticent.

"I suppose I am, but comedy and dancing are more in my line. Although my last engagement was with a repertory company at Deal, where my parents live, doing straight plays. I left them when they moved to Felixstowe. Before that I'd had two years with E.N.S.A., as well as a job in pantomime. But I only joined this company this afternoon, and I still haven't got my bearings with them. They were in the middle of rehearsal when I arrived. There's one very nice girl called Doreen, who told me that the old lady who took the money at the door is the mother of the manager, and they have a big van in which they sleep, as well as holding all the scenery and props, and that they actually do a different play every night. As there was nothing else for me to do to-night I volunteered to sell programmes."

"It all sounds a bit crazy," I said. "How on earth did you come to join such an outfit?"

"I was just bored, waiting for my agent to offer something. I saw this advertisement in *The Stage*. Experienced artistes wanted to join repertory company making tour of Cornwall, starting at Fowey. I'd never been to Cornwall, and I did want to see it. Do you live here? I think Fowey is a most enchanting place. The sea here is much bluer, and it looks warmer than at Deal. I love swimming, and boats and everything to do with the sea."

I took a deep breath.

"Look," I said; "I do live here, not here exactly but up one of the creeks leading out of the harbour. I came along this evening because I'm a writer myself, interested in the stage, and because I've got a daughter who is in a touring rep. company, encountering too, thin audiences. 'One touch of nature makes the world kin.' I thought I'd come round and talk shop with the company, and it's also true that I had a feeling I would like to meet you, for I like the way you smile."

She smiled again.

"I just can't help it. It doesn't mean a thing. It's just a nervous habit I've got. What's your name?"

I told her, and to save her embarrassment I added quickly, "It's all right. You've never heard it before!"

"I haven't, to be perfectly honest. But what a funny thing. My father is a writer too. My name's Gubbins, Stephanie. My father is . . .

"Not the famous Nathaniel!" I gasped.

"Yes."

"Then you must be Nat's Awful Child?"

"I *was*. I had an act, written by Archie de Beer for his E.N.S.A. revue *The Merry Go Round*, based on my father's character. I didn't like it very much myself, for I had to dress up like a schoolgirl and say and sing the silliest things. I was much happier when I was singing or dancing with the other girls, wearing pretty clothes, doing ballet or tap, especially tap!"

I took another deep breath. Although I was not a regular reader of the *Sunday Express*, I was a great admirer of Nathaniel Gubbins, especially during the war years. Apart from his unique brand of humour, he was a brilliant satirist and often his column contained verses of sheer poetic beauty. The Awful Child, the asker of awkward questions, Sally the Cat,

The Worm, Mr. Bumbling—I knew all of Nat's characters.
Here was The Awful Child in the flesh: and I said:

"What are you doing this evening?"

"Well, I was just going to telephone to my parents to tell them
what was happening. After that, well, I don't know. I've got
digs for the night, in a cottage. I don't know yet what the
company's plans are either. They're all in there having a sort
of conference. I don't think we'll be opening up here again
after to-night's flop."

"Right," I said. "There's a telephone kiosk just round the
corner, I'll show you where. I'm not going to try to lead
you astray. I'm a married man with a family. The fact that
my wife has not been living with me for several years is sad
but irrelevant. I may not look respectable, but I can assure
you that I am."

I had forgotten that I was dolled up. She laughed.

"I think you look quite respectable but not too much so.
I like that pullover you're wearing. What an unusual pattern."

I let that pass.

"Have you had a meal?"

"Yes, high tea at my digs. Such a darling of a landlady.
Calls me 'm'dear.' She piled lashings of food on my plate;
I think I'm going to like the Cornish."

I'd had a meal myself.

Then, "Look," I said, "unless you object, you are going to
spend the next two hours at least in my company. I'm a fan
of your father's. You can tell him that on the phone. I feel
that I have a long acquaintance with The Awful Child. It'll
be daylight for hours yet. I've got a dinghy. I can show you
the sights of Fowey from the water. We can pull up the creek
where I live. I'll not take you to my house. For one thing
I left it in a hell of a mess. For another you might misinterpret
my motives."

She laughed.

"I'd love to go in a boat."

I waited just out of hearing distance from the telephone

kiosk, in a peculiar daze of happiness, not really thinking. It was as though having got wet through and frozen with cold, I'd changed and was standing in front of a blazing fire. She came out (it must have been an over the pips' call), smiling.

"Father said he'd heard of your name, but didn't know what you had written. He wanted to know if you had long hair and a shaggy beard. Mother said I'd better be careful going out in a boat with a strange man. That a married man might be more dangerous than an unmarried one. She was only kidding. After all I'm twenty-five. Two years in E.N.S.A. playing to the troops and that followed by a tour in India with a Ralph Reader show. I can look after myself."

The tide was ebbing. I'd left the dinghy at the Albert Quay. But we hadn't turned into the main street before I felt a hand on my shoulder.

"Ahoy! Where are you off to, and who's your lady friend?"

It was Bob and Joyce. Bob wearing a tie and Joyce in a very pretty frock. We had all halted. Proudly I did the introductions. I observed that Bob was giving Stephanie a most appreciative look. I gave them a brief résumé of the evening's events, saying that I was about to take Stephanie for a pull round in the dinghy. And Bob said:

"Well, we're going to the club dance. And aren't we happy! My fortnight's holiday starts next week. Why don't you both come along too?"

With a sudden fear I asked Stephanie if there was a prospect of her leaving Fowey with the company to-morrow, which was Sunday. She said it was most unlikely. Would she like to go to the dance? I could take her in the boat in the morning. Her answer was that it would be lovely to go to a dance: and I heard myself say for the first time for so many years:

"Come on, let's all have a drink!"

There were several pubs close by. Boldly, as though I was a regular customer, I led the way into the saloon bar of the nearest one, and I wished that it could have been Polruan's Lugger or the Russell, that Arthur who had so often invited me to join him could have been with us and heard me say to him and my friends:

"What will you have?"

I knew I would have to be careful. I was already half intoxicated with sheer happiness. I didn't want to end up the evening by trying to climb the steeple of Fowey Church or the flagstaff at the Harbour Office. Bob said he'd like a lager, Joyce a port, Stephanie after some hesitation decided on a port too, and I, perhaps because during the years of abstinence I had been subconsciously impressed by the makers' very witty posters, ordered a bottle of Guinness, a drink that I had never tasted before.

We drank, we talked as coherently as possible in a room packed with other talkers. Some of these people I knew, but mostly they were visitors. We were joined shortly by mutual friends, Sean and Margaret Dorman. Sean was an Anglo-Irishman, a schoolmaster by profession but also a writer with one published novel to his credit, and another he had been labouring on for seven years. He was an uncompromising atheist, a faddist about food and health and he could never keep a teaching post for long, because he insisted on sleeping in a tent and refusing to join in school prayers.

Sean was tall, Margaret was petite, very attractive, with a Frenchwoman's flair for clothes. She had a mercurial temperament, moods of morosity associated usually with a lack of money, alternating to sometimes ecstatic gaiety. They had a family of three, a teenage boy and two attractive little girls. To-night Margaret was gay, her eyes sparkling, and she said to me:

"You beggar! How many times have I asked you to come and have a drink, and you've always said no. And how smart you look, what's happened?"

There were introductions, more incoherent talk, but Stephanie managed to say to me:

"I *do* like your friends."

Against Bob's and Sean's protests I insisted on paying for another round of drinks, but I was going easy with my Guinness and did not risk another for myself. Sean and Margaret too were going to the club, and that round finished we set out for it merrily along Fowey's main street, past the Albert Quay and then down a little alley. Like the Town Hall the club room was a story above ground level but the stairs were inside, and of wood. As we climbed them we heard the exciting sound of dance music. At the top of the stairs was Wilfred, beaming.

"Well, I'm blowed! Coming to a dance at last. What's happened to you, Leo? Who is this very charming lady?"

I introduced them, and having shaken Stephanie's hand, Wilfred at once, and with a "come on," took her on to the dance floor. I didn't mind. I didn't mind anything. Bob and Sean had taken the floor with their respective wives, as good husbands should. Keeping out of the stream of dancers, I danced a few jigs myself, not caring who saw me or if they thought I was completely tight. But I made sure that the next dance would be mine.

I think I was already in love with Stephanie. If I was, I was not conscious of it while we danced. True that it was a physical contact we were making with each other, my right arm round her waist, my left hand lightly holding hers in the strictly correct manner of ballroom dancing that I had learned at a good London school in the early days. But it was not a sexual contact. I was not a Fred Astaire or a Victor Sylvester. I had however, a good sense of rhythm, of balance and movement. And Stephanie was professional, a dancer born.

And while we danced the first and as many other numbers as Wilfred and Bob and Sean would allow, while I partnered Joyce and Margaret, we exchanged information, as Bob and I had done that first time we met, the beginning of our friendship. I wasn't trying to make love to her. As she had told me her age I told her mine, and she said, "You don't look it," and I said "I certainly don't feel it." which was true.

They were disjointed statements, like bits of mosaic which gradually would be joined into a pattern: about her family, her childhood holidays by the sea, which she had always loved,

the sea and the country. She hated towns . . . Her experiences
in E.N.S.A. . . . It was her childhood "pash" for Shirley
Temple that had given her her first yearning to go on to the
stage . . . Then it was Fred Astaire and Noel Coward who
was a friend and great admirer of her father . . . She had
flown to India in a Sunderland flying-boat. That had been
wonderful . . . Her favourite stage actors were Ralph
Richardson and Robert Donat . . . She'd loved *Oklahoma*
though and *Annie*, and Chopin was her favourite composer . . .

She had a lovely sense of humour, which was not surprising.
She had Bob's gift for mime. She gave me a perfect impersonation of a lascivious old Jewish theatrical agent who had inter-
viewed her for a job in pantomime, and asked her to show
"her tops," meaning her thighs.

Yet our conversation was not one-sided. It went backwards
and forwards, question and answer. I told her some things
about myself, why I had come back to Cornwall to live, how
my marriage had broken up, for she had asked me this, and
how I had tried in vain to mend it. I told her too what a
wonderful person my wife was, how devoted she was to our
children, and that undoubtedly she thought she was right in
leaving me because I had a bad influence on them. I even told
her that the pullover she admired had been knitted by my wife,
and sent to me as a farewell gift, and perhaps as a reward for
being a good boy about Henrietta.

I was still happy, still intoxicated. I could have gone on
dancing until daybreak. But back of my mind the idea had
already taken shape that Stephanie might come and stay to
help look after Shawn. She had told me among so many other
things that before she had joined E.N.S.A., she'd had a job
at a children's hostel. That she loved children. Shawn
I was certain would fall for her. Dare I put the proposition
to her? It would mean that she would have to leave the company for a month.

It was one of the club's rules that the Saturday night hops
should terminate Cinderella fashion at midnight, and at five

minutes to we were dancing the last waltz. Sean and Margaret and Wilfred had already gone home and Bob and Joyce were waiting at the top of the stairs.

"I'll never forgive you for this," Bob said comically as we joined them. "You've practically monopolised Stephanie the whole evening. I've just had to go on dancing with my wife."

Joyce laughed.

"Serve you right, wives aren't just for cooking meals."

And to me she said:

"Have you any news about Shawn coming?"

"Yes," I said confidently, "the end of this week."

We were on our way out. Bob said:

"We'll be sailing in the dinghy if it's a fine day to-morrow. We'll call on you round about tea-time. The tide will be just right for a swim in the cove. Is dat okay?" he added with a Yankee twang.

"Sure!" I laughed, "dat's okay. I'm taking Stephanie over to see the place to-morrow. I'll try and persuade her to stay for tea, and I'll have the vicar's tea-service out."

Stephanie's landlady had given her a latch key. We walked along to the Albert Quay, where Bob's Austin Seven was parked, dwarfed by the big chromium-plated tourers. Joyce enveloped herself in a leather coat and got in. Bob swung the starting handle and with a final "Cheerio, see you to-morrow," drove off.

We were alone.

"What a lovely couple," Stephanie said. "I think that Joyce is really beautiful. What nice friends you've got. I like Margaret and Sean, and Wilfred's a dear. It has been a wonderful evening. I have enjoyed it so."

We were standing near the rails of the quay. It was full moon, and dead calm, the tide flowing. A small coaster, with its lights reflected in the water and under its own power, was moving up-river, its wake glinting gold in the light of the moon. We watched it pass. Clear of the fairway, yachts and pleasure craft lay at their moorings, looking like so many drowsy well-fed swans. The creek from here was not visible but we could see its opening marked by a rocky bluff, and I pointed to it and said:

"It's up there where I live."

"It must be heavenly," she said, "it's all enchanting."

I took the plunge. I told her about Shawn, how I had been looking forward to his visit ever since last summer. That Henrietta had been coming to help me look after him, but that she had gone off to Canada; that a friend who had come to me before could not manage it. I had been thinking seriously of putting his visit off.

"You haven't known me more than four hours," I said. "You'll probably think I'm quite mad in asking you if you'd consider taking on for one month what would have been Henrietta's job, helping me to give my boy a happy holiday. I know you'd like him and that he'd more than like you. You could trust me so far as behaviour goes. This is practically a business proposition. And you've got your job and your career to think about. And of course you haven't seen the place yet."

She was silent for a moment, and then she said:

"I think I'd love to come. Wilfred was telling me what a lovely boy Shawn was, and he said lots of nice things about you. So did Bob and Sean when I danced with them. I was very intrigued about joining this repertory company, although when I met them I was a bit worried. I haven't got a contract. And it's going to be a profit-sharing arrangement, no regular salary. They might agree to my joining them later. It's all a bit sudden, isn't it? I'd want to think it over. Isn't it all funny that we should be standing here in Fowey and that until I saw that "ad" in *The Stage* I didn't know there was such a place." And then she said, "I hope my darling landlady isn't sitting up, waiting for the sound of the latch-key in the door."

I knew the name of the place where she was staying, only a short distance along the now deserted main street towards the station. We walked along it, close together, but not touching. And it was not until she had inserted the key in the door that she reached out her hand to mine, and said in a half whisper:

"Good night, Leo, thank you for a joyful evening. I am looking forward to to-morrow, and I think it's very very likely that I'll come and help you look after your boy."

VII

I walked back along the street with the strains of that last waltz strumming in my ears, and it was as though I was still dancing with Stephanie, for I could see her golden hair, her smile, hear her voice with its delicious chuckle.

The tide was on the turn. The dinghy was afloat, but it would be at least another hour before there would be enough water in the creek for me to land in the cove. I remembered that there was no food in the house for Choo-i. He would be at the cove to meet me, thinking that I had been fishing, and he would be disappointed if I had nothing for him. I had bait in the boat however. It was a perfect night, or rather morning, with the moon still shining, and no wind. I had no inclination to sleep. I cast off the dinghy's painter, got in, and set off down harbour, pulling as though I was in a race, with long feathered strokes, the water curling at her stem like the bow waves of a speed boat.

It was not the first time that I had pulled out to sea in the dinghy by the light of the moon when most of the people of Fowey and Polruan were in their beds, nor the first time I had been thrilled by the beauty of what I saw as I looked from right to left. The street lamps of both towns had long since been put out. Apart from the navigation lamps marking the ferry piers no other lights were visible. But the moon was so bright that I could see the colours of the painted cottage walls of Polruan, more vivid than in daylight because of the inky blackness of the shadows. The contorted rocks of the cliffs at the harbour mouth were dead black in their deep recesses, glowing with colour where they projected into the light of the moon, and there was a gleam of silver where the waves of a slow and otherwise unnoticeable ground swell broke at their foot. The actual surface of the sea was unrippled.

All this I had seen before, but always it had been with a curious feeling of selfishness, that I had no right to be enjoying it by myself. It was like gorging alone on a dish of delicious food. Now I had a sense that it was being shared, that Stephanie was with me. If she accepted my proposition, and I felt instinctively that she would, this was one of the many things she would appreciate, apart from the loveliness of the creek and the cove, the house and the garden, the little lawn, where even with a cold wind blowing up the creek it was always sheltered and warm.

I had reached the harbour mouth. I baited my trolling line and turning west under the Fowey cliff, started fishing, pulling very slowly. And as I fished I thought of how only a few hours ago I had sat at my table, looking down at the cove and the creek, contemplating packing up and leaving it all for ever.

A miracle had happened. Whatever lay beyond in time, it could be, and it *would* be, a month of happiness. It wouldn't matter a damn if Stephanie was a good housekeeper and cook, tidy, or like myself, untidy. I didn't mind housekeeping provided there was someone to housekeep for. I liked cooking provided there was someone to cook for. I didn't mind washing up, at my own sink, with its hot water supply, ample draining board and cupboard space.

The main thing was that she was youthful, good humoured, gay, nice to look at, used to, and liking the companionship of children, that she could dance and sing and mime and entertain, that Shawn would fall for her as instantly as I had done, and that she should fall for him without consciously or subconsciously alienating his affection for his own mother: for he would have to go home to her at the end of his holiday, and he, too, in a few years would be spreading his wings . . .

She liked swimming. I had a mental picture of her bathing in the cove with Shawn, racing him across the creek (I doubted if she could beat him, for last year, with his "crawl," he could have given me fifty yards start and won). I could see them in the rubber dinghy, pushing each other off, shrieking with laughter, and at meal times, and it wouldn't matter if I'd done the cooking, she would regale him with some of her "take-offs." And we'd all go fishing together, landing at Lantic or Coombe or Pridmouth, making drift-wood fires, bathing again, having picnics. And the house and the cove would once again be alive, and Bob and Joyce and our other friends would be calling . . .

I felt a tug at the line. I had almost forgotten that I was fishing. I hauled in a fair-sized pollack, Choo-i's favourite dish. I wound up the line, and started pulling energetically for home. The tide was up to the frape when I reached the cove, which with the moon lowering was in complete shadow. But I saw two glowing eyes in the dark, and as I grounded Choo-i jumped aboard and rubbed his head against my arm, mewing and purring. He knew that I had got a fish for him but he was too polite to make a grab at it, and I said to him as I tickled him under his jaw:

"Choo-i, darling! Great news for us. We're both in luck! I've got a nice juicy pollack for you, but first of all you've got to listen to what's happened to me."

He was staring hard at me with those intelligent eyes of his.

"Choo-i—Choo-i," I declaimed. "I've met an absolutely wonderful girl. Her father is a famous author who is very fond of cats, and writes about a cat he calls Sally. If I told you this is a female cat, and the mother of many kittens I am afraid that it wouldn't be of much interest to you, darling Choo-i, through no fault of your own. Anyway the great thing is that this girl, who undoubtedly likes cats, and will certainly like you and will probably want to give you more food than is good for you, and spoil you in other ways, is coming here for tea to-morrow, and if all goes well she will be coming to live here for a whole month when your dear friend Shawn will also be coming. And there's just a chance—but I won't discuss that

with you yet. We'll wait and see. Do you understand what
I am saying?"

I think that he did, for he leapt up on to my shoulder,
rubbed his head against my cheek, and if he didn't mew "yes,"
I knew that he meant it. I gave him a kiss on his ear, then
I set him down on the shingle and handed him his fish.

VIII

ON A cold, damp, foggy afternoon in the December of that year, an over-worked and tired Judge of the Probate, Divorce, and Admiralty Division of the King's Bench Division of the Judiciary of England and Wales, presiding in a gloomy upstairs court room of the Law Courts in London's Strand, pronounced what is known as a decree nisi in my favour. The whole proceeding did not last more than twenty minutes. It was a sad and in many ways a regrettable end to a marriage which for so long past its beginnings had been a happy and a successful one.

There had been no need for me to ask for the court's discretion as to my behaviour in the past. Stephanie, having most successfully and happily discharged her duties as housekeeper during Shawn's holiday, very much to Shawn's satisfaction and delight, had rejoined her repertory company which had found more appreciative audiences in the remote inland towns and villages of Cornwall where there were no cinemas, and at that time no television. But our friendship had continued, and we had met on most Sundays and on the rare days when she was without a part in the play due for performance that evening.

She had not taken her job very seriously. She was doing it more for the fun of it than anything else and certainly not for the salary, which rarely came to more than a few pounds in a week. Melodramas were the most popular of the plays performed, *East Lynne, Maria Monk, The Rosary, Jane Eyre*: a different one every night and all with only two sets, and two baskets of props.

I did not see any of these performances, but Stephanie's own account of them illustrated by extracts and miming of characters was an entertainment in itself: and already there was an understanding between us. She liked Cornwall, she liked Fowey, she liked my home, and she liked Choo-i and the way I lived, and it may be inferred that she liked me.

A month after the decree had been made absolute we were married at the local registry office with the blessing of her parents whom by this time I had met, and Wilfred acting as our best man.

There was a reception in a Fowey restaurant attended by Stephanie's charming mother Phillida (herself an ex-journalist), but not by Nat who couldn't make it because of his weekly column. Bob and Joyce were there of course, and Margaret and Sean Dorman, but not Arthur Welsh, who could not leave the ferry.

We had done our best to keep the whole thing secret. During the party however an unnamed reporter asked if he might interview us for a Press agency. We thanked him, but politely refused, and he left, not however before he had taken a quick glance at our telegrams, which Phillida had pinned up on a board. Next day several provincial and local newspapers carried the story of our marriage, giving the ages of bride and bridegroom: and giving the information that after the reception, attended by Nat Gubbins himself (Nat was in Deal) Daphne du Maurier (who had sent us a telegram from Paris), Noel Langley (who was in Hollywood and hadn't even sent a post card) Eric Portman (then starring in a London play) and many other celebrities of the literary and theatrical world, the happy couple had embarked on the bridegroom's luxury motor yacht for a honeymoon cruise along the Cornish coast. Actually we pulled home in the dinghy, taking with us a nice pollack I had bought at Percy Varcoe's for Choo-i.

Two summers later when we went to meet Shawn at the start of his holiday, we had a surprise for him.

Paradise Regained

Amanda was made fast at the Bodinnick Ferry slipway, just as she had been when I had waited so anxiously for the arrival of Henrietta. Stephanie had stayed on board. I had gone alone to the station, and I gave him no inkling of the surprise as we walked together along the station road, nor did Stephanie as they greeted each other. He stepped in. And then I said:

"Guess what's in the cabin, Shawn. It's something alive."

"Is it old Choo-i?"

"Look," I said, "look!"

He peered inside, and he said in slightly bewildered tones: "Gosh! A baby. Whose is it? Yours?"

Selina, our three-months-old daughter was in a carry-cot I had specially modified for nautical transport. There had been a gentle rain shower when we had come across the harbour, and we had pushed the cot into the cabin. Now with the sun shining again I lifted it out and lowered it on to the thwart, so that Shawn could see her clearly. He stared down at her, and she stared up at him, summing him up, as all babies do to strangers. He was dark, with black hair and brown sunburnt skin. She was fair, her hair already with a sheen of her mother's gold, her skin honey-coloured, her eyes hazel green with long dark lashes, her mouth, like Shawn's, full.

I knew that Stephanie was watching.

"Yes, she's ours," I said. "Her name's Selina, and she's what is called your half sister."

They were still staring at each other. Then Selina smiled with a baby chuckle, clawing the air with her hands. Gingerly, Shawn lowered his hand towards her. She seized one of his fingers, tried to put it in her mouth. And Shawn laughed too. It was a recognition of mutual acceptance.

"Gosh!" he said. "She *is* strong!"

And then, asserting the superiority of his sex and his years he turned to me and said:

"Is the petrol on? Shall I swing the engine for you, Daddy?"

THE END

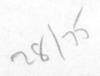

ARBROATH
PUBLIC
LIBRARY